MW00643227

Gridiron Redemption

Tommy Doles

Gridiron Redemption

Tommy Doles

© 2022 Sojourner Press

All rights reserved. No part of this publication may be reproduced, stored in a retrieval system or transmited in any form or by any means, electronic, mechanical, photocopying, recording or otherwise without the prior permision of the publisher or in accordance with the provisions of the Copyright, Designs and Patents Act 1988 or under the terms of any licence permitting limited copying issued by the Copyright Licensing Angency.

Published by: Tommy Doles

Typesetting: Julie Doles

Cover Design: Susan Doles/Julie Doles

A CIP record for this book is acailable from the Library of Congress Cataloging-in-Publication Data

ISBN-13: 978-0-578-38403-0

Printed in USA

To Bethany

mon amour et mon ami

Contents

Foreword

By Jack Doles

One of my favorite verses in the Bible is from The Parable of the Talents in Matthew 25: "Well done, good and faithful servant!"

It gives me great joy knowing that our son Tommy longs to hear those words. His life compass is pointed north, but don't think for a second he isn't open to an adventure. So I was really excited to read about THIS particular adventure.

When he was sitting in car seats, while we were driving around the country on summer road trips, Tommy never stopped asking questions. Unfortunately for us, this was before smart phones and Google. My wife, Susan, and I would make a point to get those answers. Oh, who am I kidding, Susan would make a point to get those answers. Questions were never left hanging. The mystery must be solved, or he would ask a thousand more questions. It was amazing to watch his mind work, and it has never stopped. As a journalist I ask questions and question answers for a living. But I sincerely doubt I have asked as many questions in my career as Tommy did between the ages of four to ten. So it shouldn't come as a surprise that he knows far more about pretty much everything than I do. If I need some political insight, he's a great source. If I need to know where some obscure country is, chances are, Tommy spun the globe and found it as a kid, and then learned all about what language they speak, what products they produce and if it's a democracy or dictatorship.

Another of Tommy's great passions is football. It was the perfect sport for a young man with boundless energy. It challenged him physically and mentally, and it gave him a chance to play with his friends and meet new ones. We never could have imagined where the game would take him.

Fast forward to the year 2020, and I can see that Tommy's thirst for adventure and his desire to learn are just as strong as ever. He made a name for himself on football fields around the Big Ten, but I promise that there are too many adventures to go on and dreams to chase to spend time singing one of my favorite Bruce Springsteen songs, "Glory Days" with his buddies from high school and college. I hope you didn't pick up this book to read about Grand Rapids Christian winning a state championship, or Northwestern winning the Big Ten West, or what it was like to walk into an NFL locker room. Sure, it would make for interesting reading, but what most readers crave is an adventure. Take us where we can't go, but wish we could.

Tommy had a great career, but he was knocked down at almost every turn. It happens the first time you put on the pads. You get knocked down and you have to make the choice to get up or get out. I'm proud of the way Tommy got back up every time and made a choice every player has to make at some point, but nobody wants to.

Moving on. This book is about that choice. It's about the adventure that followed. Rediscovering his love for the game and quenching his thirst for adventure at the same time. It's an adventure he shared with his new bride, Bethany, in a country not exactly known for American football. Now he shares with the rest of us. I'm confident that you'll not only enjoy the ride, but be moved by their faith and perspective.

You'll also have something to celebrate in 2020.

Being interviewed by my dad after winning the Michigan state championship in 2012.

Introduction

My phone started ringing – an unsaved number from New York. My heart raced and I smacked the steering wheel, each drum crash of the *Hawaii Five-O* ringtone giving me a little more anxiety. Driving past the old Chicago brick two-flats in my 2005 Honda CRV, I finally had to make up my mind. For months I had been torn. The recently rebooted XFL's draft was this weekend and my name was in the hat. The path back to the NFL, the next step I was *supposed* to take after getting cut. But did I want to go back?

It never should have come to this. I had essentially decided not to decide. *See if I get drafted in an early round, that will be my sign.* What a pathetic excuse for a decision! The first three rounds came and went yesterday, and I woke up hoping no one would pick me today. Hoping circumstances would make the decision for me.

But that didn't happen. My phone rang again. Then again from a different number. Three text messages floated in, congratulating me on being drafted by the New York Guardians. I hit the steering wheel again, looking for a spot I could pull off and think. This morning the CRV greeted me with a dead battery, and in a stunning act of stupidity I botched the jump, blowing a fuse. I took my fiancé *wife lol* Bethany's car to pick up a new breaker, made the switch, and finally had the car moving again. But the walls were closing in and I had to make up my mind. Where would I play football this year? Would I ever play in the NFL again? Did I have the courage to take the road less traveled, the one that was supposed to make all the difference? Cars were racing by in every direction. Bikes and scooters weaving between lanes. A thousand people on the streets. Every kind of shop imaginable. I couldn't ignore the calls forever. How did I get here?

***

My football career started with fùtbol, which I played through fourth grade. My last season was with the Aardvarks, a stacked coed club looking to make a splash in the Grand Rapids Department of Parks and Recreation Youth Soccer League. Playing defense in the final minutes of a close game, our goalie saw it fit to meet the charging striker midfield, completely abandoning the net. Thankfully, I had plenty of time to reposition in front of the net, and stood ready to protect our goal from the ball now slowly dribbling towards me from midfield. I had heroically covered for my teammate's blunder and all that was left was to pick the ball up when it rolled close enough... which of course was a handball, a penalty kick, and a tragic loss for the Aardvarks. Perhaps losing faith in my ability to earn a soccer scholarship someday, my parents gave in and allowed me to sign up for football the next year.

There's little nuance, strategy, or elegance to youth football. Top heavy school boys waddle up to the field under bulky helmets and shoulder pads, having a grand old time running around for two hours, just happy to be out there and call themselves football players. With a frame growing faster than my coordination could keep up with, I was stuck on the line for most of my youth career. My proudest moment may have been when a coach told me I looked like Brian Urlacher after a short haircut I'd gotten hoping to hear just that. We proudly wore our black jerseys to school on Fridays in the fall and obsessively cheered on the varsity team later under the lights, knowing we would do our part to uphold the pride of the community Saturday morning. I fell in love with the idea of being a football player. Of being on a team that worked hard and with a purpose. It was difficult and exciting! The spectacle of high school football was all my imagination had room for at the time, forget anything beyond that.

High school football finally came around, and my jaw dropped when I walked into the weight room and saw how much growing I still had to do. A fourteen-year-old isn't in the same ballpark physically as an eighteen-year-old, and I couldn't imagine myself ever being up to the task of competing against these men! I distinctly remember my stomach sinking when I saw a junior's calves, which seemed impossibly thick compared to my scrawny members. I knew then and there that I would never play varsity football. But time goes on, you work hard, listen to your coaches, drink two-percent milk, and nature runs its course. I started gaining weight and diving into the game. It was fast and complicated, but I realized I could handle it with some work and coachability. I still didn't think I'd ever make it to JV, let alone varsity, until one morning when head coach Don Fellows pulled me aside before a morning workout and told me I'd be joining the varsity squad for the last game of the season and the playoffs.

Don Fellows has been one of the most impactful people in my life. As freshmen, we were fascinated by him, but terrified. With dark hair and a shadow that came through before his aftershave was dry, he showed up at 6:00 AM workouts totally put together in black slacks and a golf shirt. He brought more intensity than we'd ever seen before. You could see it in his eyes, and straightened your posture when he looked at you. No one got a free pass for making a mistake, or much worse, slacking off.

More than investing in my development as a football player, Fellows changed who I was as a person. I grew to love challenges, walk with confidence, control my thinking, truly work hard, and do it all with my faith at the center. Coach Fellows believed in me more than I ever believed in myself. Before I had dreamed bigger than seeing the field as a varsity football player, he told me I had Division I talent. *What now?* I may have floated the idea of playing for the Division III Coast Guard Academy after watching Kevin Costner's rescue swimmer film, *The Guardian*, a dream that seemed audacious in its own right, but Division I wasn't even in the picture.

What Fellows saw and nurtured early on came to fruition as time passed. I started my sophomore year at left tackle, improved my game over the season, and ended with All-Conference honors. Junior year it was All-State. In a moment that will never fall from my lifetime highlight reel, we won the Michigan Division III 2012 State Championship. When you're sixteen, running onto Ford Field[1] with your closest friends, you can't possibly imagine life getting any better. By my senior year, I was totally in love with the game and everything about high school.

---

1   The Detroit Lions' home stadium

The recruiting process began in force the summer after my sophomore year, and didn't stop until I committed to Northwestern the next spring. The courtship process between college football programs and promising sixteen-year-olds can be outright bizarre. I'd have stacks of mail in my locker every day, sometimes as simple as a picture of Urban Meyer sitting on the Westeros Iron Throne captioned, *FALL IS COMING!* We had acne and minimum wage summer jobs, but were prized cattle to billion-dollar football programs. The University of Michigan was the first school to offer me a scholarship, but the idea of playing college football was new enough that I wasn't ready to make a decision just yet.

I visited West Point and Northwestern, and loved them both. I decided to defer my desire to serve in the military, ruling out West Point. Having settled on playing in the Big Ten, it came down to Michigan and Northwestern. Michigan is a top public university and fields one of college football's marquee programs. However, for reasons that were hard to nail down, I felt myself fitting in better at Northwestern. Headed by Northwestern alum and College Football Hall of Fame linebacker Pat Fitzgerald, the Wildcats emphasized character, academic excellence, their proximity to Chicago, and an offense my skills fit into. Current and former players assured me the ideals espoused in the recruiting pitch weren't window dressing. Northwestern seemed like a place where all of me could thrive. The tuba player, the social studies nerd, the offensive lineman, the musical theatre fan. As I was falling in love with Northwestern, Michigan was getting tired of waiting, and stopped recruiting me. On May 3, 2013, I called Coach Fitzgerald and told him I was in. I've been bleeding purple ever since.

College brought about its share of troubles. I was once again undersized and insecure. I had hip surgery and sat out my freshman year. I struggled to understand calculus; my high school sweetheart broke up with me. My grandpa died and I missed his funeral. I got pushed around in practice and wondered if I'd ever see the field. I missed my family and friends from home. We lost games and people asked why I didn't go to Michigan.

But as time passes since leaving Evanston, the sad and difficult memories of my early days fade away, leaving visions of an idyllic five years. I remember summers filled with purposeful workouts and engaging lectures. Weekends playing beach volleyball, making ice cream runs, and laughing into the night with my best friends in a house we rented off campus. I don't think of those early months at the bottom of the totem pole, when I was nervous, insecure, and didn't think my full self would ever come out again. No, I think of impeccable landscaping next to the lake and bible studies on Sunday nights. Late night moped adventures along the North Shore. A Capella concerts and cookouts. A mysterious chill in the October air before the gothic homecoming parade. Strolling the library gardens. Position group dinners on Thursday nights, when the whole restaurant looks at the towering group walking in. Maybe they wish us luck on Saturday or ask to take a picture. Late night spiritual conversations in the dorms.

I remember linking arms with the other captains and walking to midfield for the coin toss. Marching into hostile stadiums and returning to campus victorious. Proud parents embracing you after a win, talking about where we'd go for dinner. Walking into church the next morning with a soreness you felt good about. Trying new restaurants. Or going back to Chipotle. Watching the sun rise over the lake from the new weight room. Catching an Amtrak home for Christmas with stories to tell. Meeting Bethany and falling in love. Fairytale dates in Lincoln Park. Wonder. Museums. Outdoor movies. Campfires. Road trips to fine hotels and great stadiums. Bowl games and the Big Ten Championship. A brotherhood. The constant feeling of being *the man in the arena*, of spending yourself for a worthy cause.

Perhaps this is why it was difficult for me to move on to the NFL. I had found a home and loved it dearly, yet five years later it was time to wake up from the dream. I knew this was coming, and how could I argue with time? But leaving still hurt. Halas Hall, the Chicago Bears facility in Lake Forest, was forty minutes from my house in Evanston, but it felt like a world away. One Sunday night on my way back for another week of OTAs, [2] I stopped by to see my friends from the bible study. We laughed, ate, and caught up. *Home again!* But when the time came to head downstairs for their study, I had to go. I felt the full weight of the moment, driving north on I-94 with the golden sun illuminating the road. Tears flowed as I thanked God for that community and the new opportunities I had, but asked him why time had to move forward, so steady and incessant. A new season of life had started, like it or not.

Finding my way into the NFL wasn't a smooth process, and neither was my time as a professional. My college career ended in cinematic fashion: standing in the rain on a podium in San Diego, celebrating a historic come from behind victory in the Holiday Bowl. I got engaged to the love of my life the next day at Sunset Cliffs Natural Park. Following what were easily the best twenty-four hours of my life, I embarked on the stressful process of finding an agent, which filled me with doubts about my abilities I hadn't felt since I was a fifteen-year-old starting the recruiting process.

Finding an agent is like an old fashioned courtship. The fairer the lady, the more suitors there were. An agent spends time marketing you and puts up the cost

---

2   Organized Team Activities, NFL preseason practieces without shoulder pads

of training for your pro day. [3] If you're unlikely to give them a return on their investment, they steer clear. I was on the fringe, projected to go undrafted, but with a shot nonetheless. Several agents had reached out to me, with varying degrees of professionalism and resources. One seemed promising early on, and even spent an hour on Facetime with my parents and me, but later called and pulled out. He didn't want the risk. Most of the phone calls stressed me out. Someone I didn't know musing about whether or not I had what it took to make them money.

The time to train for pro day started, and I still didn't have an agent. Unless I started soon, I'd be left behind. Without the funds to train at Chicagoland's most popular elite training center, I did a Google search for others, calling around to see who could work with me. That's when I found EFT in Highland Park. Run by Elias Karras, a papa-bear style former power lifter, EFT became my second home for the next three months. Elias let me join the combine prep group right away. Not only did he hold off on charging me until I found an agent, he connected me with one he trusted and who became one of my great friends – Bob Engler.

Bob is a smart, well-dressed New Yorker with an infectious smile and unmatched attitude. He agreed to work with me and told me he would do everything he could to help me pursue this dream. I first met Bob in Orlando, where I had traveled for the week as a Big Ten delegate to the NCAA convention. He picked me up from my hotel in a Porsche and we sped over to The Capital Grille. With a shiny bald head and round dimples, Bob was as excited as I was about the journey ahead, and made sure I tried the lobster bisque soup.

---

3 A chance to work out in front of NFL scouts. Top prospects are invited to the NFL combine.

For the next three months, I spent my mornings at EFT, working out and rehearsing combine drills with a group of seven other hopefuls from around the Midwest, under the tutelage of Kerry Neal, a former Notre Dame defensive lineman turned combine prep guru. [4] After three hours of training, Blake Hance and I would jet downtown for an afternoon of grad school classes. Cone drills and corporate finance. Blake, a central Illinois native and Northwestern's left tackle for the past four years, became a great friend of mine through college, but even more this spring. Between EFT and Kellogg, I spent significantly more time with him during these months than anyone else. During our high speed drives down I-94, we might listen to oldies music, Stuff You Should Know podcasts, or just review the cash flow statement.

Without an invite to the combine, Northwestern's pro day was my only shot to impress the NFL scouts. Clayton Thorson, my former roommate and close friend, was the main draw. A stalwart career running the offense left him as Northwestern's leading passer, winningest quarterback, and America's college football player with the most career starts. Ever. Clayton throwing meant every team would be there, and they stuck around to watch the rest of us give it a shot too.

They paraded us in front of an auditorium full of serious middle-aged men with clipboards and branded polos, wearing nothing but our underwear. A strange burlesque show of sorts. After months of constant training, you had one, *maybe two*, shots at each drill. There's a special sense of anticipation before the forty-yard-dash, the most storied event of the day, which can make or

---

4 Kerry happened to have played in the first college football game I ever attended. In 2010, the Irish hosted Western Michigan and I joined my dad, a sports broadcaster for the NBC affiliate station in Grand Rapids (WOODTV-8), in the press box. I decided that day that I would never be as big as those titans and might as well give up on playing football at a high level.

break your chances of being drafted. You ease into the starting position you've gotten so sick of practicing and look downfield, narrowing your focus as everyone goes quiet.

Go!

There's a surreal feeling while you eat up the ground, hearing nothing but your breath and cleats hitting the turf, so confident that this will be the fastest run of your life. At the end of the day my numbers were good, but not great. Certainly not good enough to catapult me to the top of anyone's draft board.

I spent day one of the NFL draft with friends, enjoying the spectacle and laughing when a sack I gave up in the Big Ten Championship game looped on ESPN after the Broncos drafted Ohio State's Dre'Mont Jones. Day two I hoped Clayton would get drafted in an early round. Day three started checking my phone in a Global Finance lecture, secretly hoping I'd be picked in a late round, and ended sitting in my house with Bethany, anxiously awaiting a phone call that never came. Bob Engler called after the draft, sharing my disappointment but happy to report I had been invited to rookie minicamp by the Bears and the Saints. Minicamp was a chance for teams to onboard their draft picks, and bring in some long shots who just might get signed to the ninety-man roster at the end of a grueling weekend. I'd train with the Bears next weekend, and if I wasn't signed, try my hand in New Orleans the following.

Minicamp started early with twenty linemen tensely trying to look tough while waiting for the coach to walk into the meeting room. Uninterested in such an environment, I offered that we used to make freshmen tell jokes when it got too quiet, and offered one of my all-time favorites.

"What do you call a fake noodle?.......an *impasta*."

I received a mix of courtesy laughs and blank stares. Then I was one upped by a shockingly inappropriate joke from another lineman, to the absolute delight of the room. Some normal conversation flowed from there. The rest of the weekend was a mix of focused meetings, intense walkthroughs, and violent practices. The pressure was real and incessant, most of it courtesy of Harry Hiestand. Considered one of the best offensive line coaches in the business, Hiestand knew what he wanted and exactly how he wanted it done. He was very clear about his role in our lives.

"You've got a mom, a girlfriend, or whatever else in your life to make you happy and feel good, but I'm the only one in your life whose job it is to make you a better football player. I have no interest in making you feel good, I only care about making you a better offensive lineman, and you should be thankful for that."

Old school through and through, he was very much of the opinion that the best linemen are forged by high expectations and extreme pressure. Think of Terence Fletcher from *Whiplash* coaching football. By the end of the weekend, I was having dreams about Hiestand yelling at me for holding the hand shield the wrong way while I stood in on defense for individual drills. Excessive attention from a coach, however, usually means you're doing something right. Or at least, they think you could do something right eventually. At Northwestern, Coach Cushing[5] used to say that you should be worried when you do something wrong and don't get yelled at, because that means the coaches are moving on. As I walked off the field after the last practice of the weekend, thinking about New Orleans next week, one of the scouts looked up from his phone, pulled me aside, checked my number to confirm he had the right guy and said,

---

5 My offensive line coach at Northwestern and now the head coach at Eastern Illinois

"Okay Doles after you get changed, head to the ATR and wait to get a physical. Assuming you pass, head upstairs and we're gonna sign you."

Just like that, he walked off and I was about to become a Chicago Bear. Well, the ninetieth man on a roster that would be cut down to fifty-three before anyone got seriously paid, but we'd worry about that later. For now, I could find my name on the roster. I could wear the gear. I had a W-2 from *Chicago Bears Football Club, Inc.* After showering I talked to Bob, who had already reviewed the contract.

"Standard rookie deal, three years, one point seven-five million dollars, zero guaranteed. Congrats, I knew you'd do it. You ready to go sign an NFL contract?"

I went upstairs, signed it, shook hands with the general manager, and hit the road for a wedding shower. Driving west into the late afternoon sun, I called my dad. Born just outside of Chicago in River Grove, my dad had raised me as a Bears fan. As long as I can remember, we had shared our passion for the team, and would root them along every Sunday afternoon. I wore an Urlacher jersey to school Mondays after a win. Posters covered the walls in my bedroom. I shared the news. He was thrilled, he was proud. The pleasure of telling him was undergirded by the knowledge that his love was unconditional, and cool as this was, failure wouldn't have changed that. Then I called Bethany and my mom, letting them know I was on my way to the shower and had just signed an NFL contract. I got there and we celebrated with summery finger food, champagne, and the first of many *Bed Bath and Beyond* boxes.

One week later I was packing a duffle bag in Evanston, preparing to drive up to Lake Forest, check into a hotel, and begin my NFL career early the next morning. My phone rang: Ryan Pace, the Bears general manager.

"Tommy, we had to make a roster move. As you know we've been shuffling kickers around, and we cut you to make space for another one. Stay ready, stay in shape, because we want you back."

Apparently they didn't tell Harry Hiestand, who, I was later told, fumed for two minutes past the scheduled start of the Monday morning meeting before storming out of the room cursing my name and Northwestern University, only to come back five minutes later and start the film session as if nothing were amiss – presumably having just caught up with Mr. Pace.

Thus began my tumultuous NFL career. I was signed for exactly one week and attended zero practices, but I'd been cut. Not to worry, Bob called me three days later while on the porch working my way through a Business Strategy case assignment.

"We're back with the Bears. They want you to get up there as soon as you can."

I drove back up to Lake Forest and the work began. I studied, trained, played, and recovered from football every waking moment. I'd drink a Pedialyte and read for a few minutes before bed, just to clear my head. Rather than walking through the locker room as a senior team captain, I was the low man on the totem pole. Even the equipment managers seemed more comfortable than I did.

Slowly but surely I built relationships and learned my way around the playbook. On the first off night the other rookie linemen and I went out to a pizza place Olin Kreutz[6] recommended we try. We ate, drank, laughed, and unwound. People came by the table and told us *go Bears*. These rookie linemen became my closest circle. *Close* is relative, however. It all felt new and shallow compared

---

6   A future Hall of Fame center for the Bears and one of my favorite players growing up.

to my friendships at Northwestern. But nonetheless, we survived together and dreamed of making the cut.

At the time, I was counting down the days with vigor. In less than two weeks, I would be done with OTAs, marrying Bethany, and leaving the pressure behind for a week in Jamaica. But I was cut loose for the summer sooner than expected. In the morning before practice, I noticed two scouting assistants walk into the locker room. Anyone who's not a sure bet to make the team looks away and prays they don't come towards them. They headed in my direction, and focusing on tying my shoes, I pretended they weren't there until I heard,

"Hey Tommy coach needs to see you upstairs, bring your iPad and playbook."

So I was being cut again. The Vikings released a veteran lineman last night and the Bears grabbed him off of waivers. It was a business and when someone better becomes available, they make room. As I finished my exit physical exam, the team excitedly streamed back from the meeting room, much earlier than expected. For morale, Coach Nagy cancelled practice and meetings for the day, and the team was headed to Top Golf. Not me. I turned in my things and drove back to the hotel. I'd gotten to know the man at the front desk. Surprised to see me back early, he reared back in empathy upon hearing the news, cursing the Bears and offering me a coffee. I never drink coffee, but couldn't say no to the gesture. I sat in the room for a while, finishing the snacks I stashed away and wondering what to do next. As one does when they get fired, I drove to Wendy's for a spicy chicken sandwich, found the nearest nature preserve and ate it while looking at some birds. The quiet was nice.

Ding!

Fans were already tweeting jokes and memes about my hectic tenure with the team.

I can't complain about any of the days that followed. I spent time with family, traveled, finished my master's degree, and on July seven, made a covenant with Bethany before God, our families, and two hundred of our closest friends. After a fairytale wedding in Chicago and a perfect week in Jamaica, we were snatched back to reality by a very pressing question.

Now what?

We were both unemployed, technically homeless, and Bethany had deferred medical school for a year to join me on this football ride. Our wedding gifts were in a ten by ten storage unit in Marengo, [7] and we had a week's worth of beach clothes in two suitcases. We got a pass from being bums, given that Bethany was bound for medical school and I had recently been an NFL player, but that wouldn't last forever. The closest thing we had to a plan was this: once NFL training camps got underway, there would be injuries, and renewed demand for people like myself to fill in the gaps and keep the machine moving. We would accept the generosity of family and friends until I got a call. One week in my aunt and uncle's Chicago apartment. One week house sitting for friends in Evanston. Just as we were getting antsy, Bob called again.

"The Falcons need another lineman. They're bringing you and another guy in for a workout. Pack like you could be there for a month, but you might be back in Chicago tomorrow night. Good luck."

An hour later I was headed for O'Hare, rushing to board a flight to Atlanta. A scouting assistant picked me up in a silver Mercedes sprinter van and brought me to a hotel. Early the next morning I got into the same van with the other lineman I'd be competing against for the job. It was a zero-sum game, but he was a delightful person. I'm sure we would have been friends if we played

---

7   Bethany's home town, northwest of Chicago

together. We got physicals, drove to the facility in Flowery Branch, and hit the field for a series of rapid fire drills with Chris Morgan, the offensive line coach. What they were looking for and saw in me, I'm not exactly sure, but an hour later I was signing a new contract during the heart of training camp.

My three weeks with the Falcons were challenging but tremendous. I joined a team that played loose, enjoyed the process, and didn't take itself too seriously. I went from Harry Hiestand to a coach who kept a soundboard on hand during meetings. Bethany visited and we explored Atlanta. I spent time with my Atlanta-based Uncle Jim and Aunt Jana. I traveled with the team to Miami for a preseason game. I suited up in Mercedes Benz stadium to play Washington. [8] I liked it there and wanted to stay. But the fun came to an end one off day with a phone call summoning me to the coach's office, just as Bethany and I were walking into the Georgia Aquarium. I knew the drill by now. Bring you iPad and playbook. We landed in Chicago later that night.

My NFL career wasn't over yet – Chicago claimed me the next day off of waivers. [9] I had one more go around with my old friends from the Bears, culminating in a Soldier Field showdown against the Titans where I held my own on the field goal unit. Two days later the grim reaper made his rounds across the NFL for final cuts. My iPad and playbook were ready to go.

Things were different now. Across the league, thirty-two teams had cut their rosters from ninety to fifty-three. That meant there were 1,184 fewer NFL jobs than the day before. I could keep working out and asking

---

8   A team that included, at the time, none other than Blake Hance.

9   For a period of time after a player is cut, another team can "claim" him off of waivers, meaning they take over the most recent contract he was cut from. If no one claims you, you'll become a free agent.

Bob to talk to teams, but the odds were slim that I'd be getting another call. Rookies have the preseason to give it their best shot, but beyond that, teams either look to veteran players or the next crop of talent. If you didn't stick the first time around, it would take something special to get back into the pipeline.

Back in Chicago, Bethany and I pondered our options. The natural choice was the XFL. After fizzling out in 2001, Vince McMahon was rebooting the league he had originally conceived of as an edgy competitor to the NFL. In its first iteration, the league toed the line of gimmicky sports entertainment, a brand that made McMahon's fortune with the WWE. This time around, the league presented itself as a more serious second tier American league, catering to a population of athletes I was now a part of – talented players unwanted by the NFL, but with some ball left to play. The league paid a fraction of an NFL contract, but was competitive with a normal entry level job. It promised to be exciting, innovative, and the best path back to the NFL.

I'd likely be drafted, which meant another month of training camp and rounds of cuts before the opener in February. Deep down I had little interest in playing in the XFL. My body ached, unable to fathom another month of intense training camp. I wondered if the internal fire that had always driven me as a football player was starting to dim. Bethany's medical school wouldn't hold her spot for another year, so in the unlikely event the NFL called me back after the XFL season, I wasn't sure I'd take another shot at it. Deep down, I realized that this would be my last year of football.

How should I spend the last few drops of myself I was prepared to give to the game? I didn't want it to be with the XFL. But it wasn't that easy. You see, for the past nine years, I had been on a highway, driving in the fast lane. Football took me to new heights every year. I had been in the top tier of my peers since Coach Fellows pulled me up to varsity in 2010. But now, I had taken an exit; I sat stationary on the side of the road, watching friends and former teammates continue on in the fast lane towards NFL rosters and fat game checks. *Who was I if I wasn't on that highway?*

Thankfully, I had spent plenty of time thinking about this question over the years, largely with the help of Athletes in Action (AIA), a Christian organization that serves as a spiritual resource for college, professional, and Olympic athletes. I knew that my identity came from being made in the image of God. Being loved by him enough that he died the death I deserve for my sins. That through faith I could accept Jesus' sacrifice on my behalf and be forgiven, eternally reconciled to God. And that these truths ought to radically change my life, including the way I competed in my sport. None of these truths were contingent on my performance as an athlete. I was free.

It was a friend from AIA, coincidentally, who pointed me towards a different path forward. I had met Tyler Warner years ago at an AIA event in Chicago, and vaguely knew that he did something with football overseas. I called him shortly after getting cut and explained my situation.

"We're having a combine in Ohio later this month for guys asking the same questions." He told me. "You should really come, I think you'll be glad you did."

Unsure what I was getting myself into, I drove to Xenia, Ohio for a week at The Total Athlete Combine. What I had kicked myself for committing to on the long drive down, thinking it might be waste of time, turned out to be one of the most life-giving weeks I've ever experienced. Instead of angry coaches reminding me I was on the fringe, I was unconditionally welcomed and encouraged. The staff's goal was to build us up and they demanded nothing in return. In five days I connected more with the nine players and four staff members than I did with anyone in my months around the NFL. The idea was to prepare us to play in international professional football leagues, using our position to share the love of Christ with teammates who may have never heard this good news. We ate, trained, and played mini-golf together. We learned about sports psychology, cross cultural competency, finding international teams, and how to share our faith. By the end of the week I had new friends and a fresh vision for how I could spend this last year of football.

But the highway hadn't left. Driving back to Chicago, I couldn't shake the feeling that I *should* declare for the XFL draft. That's what everyone assumed I would do. They talked about how exciting it was that I'd play a part in the reboot of the NFL's slick younger brother.

"I can't wait to get my Doles XFL jersey! I hope you end up in New York. Maybe you'll meet Vince! You'll be back in the NFL in no time."

"Yeah, umm, that'd be pretty cool. I guess we'll see." I was completely torn inside.

The XFL could be a great experience. I might make friends and have a great time. But it filled me with dread when I thought about it. I felt jaded. I'd been chewed up and spit out by the American football machine. Football was a business now, not a family. To me, the XFL looked like more of the same. The thought of finding a team overseas, however, filled me with wanderlust and excitement. *So why was it still so hard?*

Ian Park was Northwestern's right guard before I had my three years of fun. He hosted me on my first visit and quickly became a good friend. After an injury ended his senior season, the NCAA denied Ian an extra year of Division I eligibility. Not to be dissuaded, he transferred to Slippery Rock, a Division II program near his home in Pittsburgh. Following a dominant year, he had his shot at the next level and spent training camp with the Philadelphia Eagles. Unfortunately, a concussion sidelined him during the preseason, and he was cut. Never one to care much what others thought, but still in love with the game, Ian's next contract was with the Lixil Deers of Japan's X-League. With few friends who could understand my unique situation, I reached out to talk it over.

"Tommy no one's making you play football anymore. You don't need to do this for a scholarship and unless you're in the league, you can make more money doing something else. Do what you actually want. I've had enough of football in North America and have no plans to leave Japan anytime soon."

***

I pulled off onto a shady, quiet side street and called Bethany. She trusted me and believed we'd make it work either way. I called my dad. My parents loved me and would support me no matter what. They were proud of me and said to go with my gut. No pressure. I leaned back, looking at the gentle fall leaves with tears welling in my eyes. Saying no would mean saying no to any hope of returning to the NFL. I'd be retiring, shedding the identity of an elite football player that I was holding onto by a thread. But under the swaying autumn trees, I finally felt peace. I called the coach back.

"This is Tommy Doles getting back to you. I'm sorry for the delay and sorry to put you in this position, but I'm not going to play in the XFL this year. I wish you the best."

Relief. I sat in stunned silence, trying to understand what just happened. I was no longer an elite football player. I was conclusively and forever off of the highway.

I just cut football loose, and it was floating away. But I was free. Free to chart a new course. It was terrifying and thrilling, like I had broken a rule and gotten away with it. If I wanted any part of the game, I'd need to rediscover it somewhere else. I closed my eyes and smiled as I imagined where that somewhere might be.

***

If you were paying close attention in your high school American Literature class, you may still be seething from an earlier reference. A favorite bubble to pop among English teachers? Robert Frost's The Road Not Taken doesn't mean what you think it does! Rather than proclaiming the merits of courageously going against the grain, Frost describes two roads not too different from one another that eventually lead to the same spot. You could write a book analyzing it, but the poem mocks the weight we see in our decisions, inviting the reader to either chill out, or spiral downward into the gloom of nihilism. [10] Was choosing Paris a bold resolution to go against the grain and into the unknown? Or perhaps a fool's errand that would leave me in the same spot a year from now? I certainly had no idea at the time, but was ready to try a croissant at the nearest bakery.

---

10 In short, nothing matters

Warming up before one of my last football games (in America!).

CHAPTER I

Onboarding

Tuesday, January 7, 2020 – Arrival

I've got a lot of feelings, looking down on the dark Atlantic from my Lufthansa coach seat. The cabin lights had dimmed. Most of the passengers on the Chicago to Frankfurt red-eye slept, but I was stewing. I like to write off mistakes as learning opportunities, but when you fork over $138 for an overweight bag, that's a tough argument to make. The bag was stuffed with more books than I could possibly read, a fitting symbol for my head at the moment. I'd built up a colossal list of things to learn, see, and do in the next seven months, and it was starting to intimidate me. I would read two dozen books, master French, learn Biblical Greek, see everything in Europe, evangelize the entire team, and take my marriage to new heights in the city of love, not to mention fall in love with football again and lead the Flash to a championship.

After a short layover in Frankfurt, I was bound for Paris. The Flash paid for my flight, but didn't have it in the budget to fly Bethany over, so she'd be joining me a week later on a cheaper flight we found. It's rare a team will sign a married import. Apparently there have been enough bored significant others wanting to leave early, that the safe bet is to stick with bachelors. Thankfully, we convinced the Flash that Bethany was every bit as excited about Paris as I was, and wouldn't be dragging me home midseason.

Walking past customs into the main terminal, I hoped I'd recognize Bruno. Bruno Lacam-Caron was with the Flash when the club formed in 1983. Once a player, he's long since hung up the cleats and now serves as the general manager. I spotted him immediately when I walked out. Typing on his phone and occasionally looking up so he didn't miss me, Bruno looked the part. He had the build of a former football player and a bright red Washington State hoodie, but with a clean bald head and fashionable glasses, he meant business too.

"Tommy, welcome to Paris." He greeted me with clear but distinctly accented English.

"Merci beaucoup, je suis tres content... uh, to be ici." [1] I replied in my pitiful French.

He laughed and we shook hands.

"It's okay, you will get better. We will wait for James to arrive and then get you to your new home. You must be very tired."

I was excited but a bit nervous to meet James. As the only other American and native English speaker on the team, not to mention my left guard, this relationship would have a big impact on my experience.

While Bruno ordered me a croissant with green tea, I met his wife, Mariannick. [2] Mariannick runs the office and coaches the cheerleaders. No one would accuse

---

1 *"Thank you very much, I am happy to be here."*

2 *Marie-a-neek*

her of being bubbly, but I could tell she had a kind heart and wanted me to feel welcome.

"You will see your room soon. It is not big, not big at all, but you know this. I hope that you will like it. I buy.. how to say.. *supplies!* Yes, for the kitchen and new sheets for bed. You will have the double room because your wife comes too yes?"

As we talked, I bit into an unfathomably wonderful piece of bread. The flaky shell gave way to a soft and buttery inside I could have shed a tear over. Call me a nationalist, but I'm not one to say a country does something better than the United States just because "the powers that be" seem to think so. I will, however, concede absolute defeat in the pastry arena. I don't know how there can be such a difference with a simple piece of bread.

Football players, offensive linemen in particular, have a remarkable ability to bond quickly. Whether it stems from unique shared experiences or the personality types the position draws, James and I were no exception. We got up to speed on each other's background and playing history. Hailing from Long Island, New York, James stayed close to home, playing at Long Island University, a Division II powerhouse that made the jump to Division I after he left. At 6'3, 310lbs, James stood out amongst the Parisians in Charles de Gaulle Airport as much as I did. He had dark hair, glasses, a scraggly beard, and a face that told me he'd be easy to get along with. It wasn't long before we moved past the football pleasantries and shared more about our lives. In the car, we talked on and off while taking in the new environment rolling past us. James noticed my ring.

"Hold on, are you *married*??"

"Yeah we got married last July, she's coming over in a week."

I imagine this came as a surprise, and wonder if he was worried he'd soon be losing his one American friend like Timone and Pumba lost Simba.

"She's really cool, you'll like her and we'll all have to check out Paris soon. So what's Long Island like? I've never been there."

"Brooo!" He leaned forward and clapped. "You *gotta* come visit sometime. We got this place called Bubba's that's *mad* good. Check it out, they got a burrito, right? But it's full of fried chicken tenders, mozzarella sticks, bacon, cheese, hot sauce, and some special sauce. They call it The Guilt Trip."

We spent the rest of the afternoon settling in. Our new home was a little dorm building on the edge of a public athletic complex, *Stade de Mode*, complete with soccer fields, basketball courts, and, as it so happens, a small BMX track. Our building contained thirteen rooms (*chambres*), a small laundry room (*buanderie*), and a security office. Next to the gate, there was a satellite building with a kitchen and dining space (*cuisine*). Our double room was about the size of a single American dorm, leaving James' single in the realm of a large closet.

According to Mariannick, who was showing us around, we'd be sharing the facility with an eclectic group of athletes.

"Different teams live in Stade de Mode. You have women's rugby, athletics,[3] American football, and one soccer player I think. But we give you special closet so the rugby girls do not take your food. Yes, we give you extra space."

She led us into an austere storage closet that had been retrofitted into a pantry of sorts. A folding table with a dish rack, some basic silverware, and a few hand towels. There was a refrigerator too, flanked by stacks of linens, pillows, and extra mattresses.

---

3 Track and field

"You have the car to use when you like," Bruno informed us, "we get automatic car, because Americans in the past, they see manual and don't know what to do, like they never see a clutch before and they break it. So now we have this. We give you train passes too, there is lots and lots of public transport in Paris."

"But be careful," Mariannick interjected, "to go on strike is the national pastime of France. The trains might run, they might not run. It just depends on how pissed off the workers are at Macron." [4]

Having kept up my streak of never sleeping on planes, I was exhausted. Back in the dorm, I realized there'd be no communications tonight, seeing as I had no local phone plan and useless WI-FI. I caught a brief second wind and realized how empty the bed felt without Bethany. I had only been married for six months, but grown so used to having her with me. The last fumes of energy soon passed and I was asleep in my new home.

Wednesday, January 8, 2020 – The Americans are here

In our WhatsApp group, Paul told James and me he'd pick us up around eleven to start the day. Paul Durand was the first person I spoke with from the Flash and wears many hats for the club. I met him as the recruiter, learned he was also the offensive coordinator, and finally that he led the team on field as our quarterback. He was tall, lean, had shaggy dark hair, and the unmistakable but unassuming swagger of a savvy athlete. He wore a black and yellow Flash hoodie with gray sweatpants. A bulge in his pocket gave away a smoking habit that we found all too common among Europeans.

Paul pulled up in a small black Peugeot and hurriedly climbed out to greet us.

---

4 The President of France, Emmanuel Macron

"Whats up, guyeees!" He exclaimed in a laid back voice.

"Paul! Comment ca va?" [5] I attempted.

"You want to speak French, that is good! I show you how normal French people talk. Just say, 'ca va.' [6] Anyways, we go to your physical now and then we will go to practice. You won't put on your pads this time, but can still watch and run with us."

Stade de Mode was in Bobigny, a town in the prefecture of Seine-Saint-Denis, a large suburb just north of Paris.

"You live in Bobigny, we drive through La Courneuve now, where the Flash play, and then to Momo's office in Saint-Denis. Momo volunteers to be the team doctor, he is very good. He likes to meet the Americans before we start."

Paul pointed out a massive stadium approaching on our left.

"This is *Stade de France*, where the French national soccer team plays. Momo is their doctor also. He is very good."

Walking up to the office, I was lost in thought, looking around at the buildings when Paul grabbed my arm.

"Take care, there is something.. *disgusting*."

I looked down. In front of me was an oozing pile of something brown. It must have come out of a small bear, or, I fear, a homosapien.

The physical itself, if you could call it that, lasted all of two minutes. An older doctor with a large build, Momo gave us a once over and seemed to think everything looked alright. He didn't speak any English with us, but quipped in rapid French to Paul.

---

5 *"How are you?"*

6 *"You good?"*

"He says you two are so big and I must be scared as quarterback so I recruit big linemen. He is not wrong, I am a pocket passer. You say.. a *gun-slinger*! I don't like to get hit! But maybe I will surprise you with my legs sometimes."

Next it was back to La Courneuve for our first visit to the Flash facilities. Housed in *Stade Geo Andre*, the Flash occupied the top of an old four story brick building covered in ivy.

"Tommy I see your Northwestern facility on Twitter.. wowwwa. I am sorry this won't be that. But we have office and film room in the building, and there is the field to the right." He pointed towards a stand of bleachers with doors to locker rooms underneath. "We share Geo Andre with lots of people. Soccer, rugby, tennis, and some other stuff."

"Yo do we drive here for practice?" James asked.

"Ahh, yes you can drive but I suggest you take the street train. That is the best way to come. Get on in front of the hospital by Stade de Mode, and get off just across the street over there."

Once practice started, James and I did our best to keep up. A flurry of shouting suggested the warmup was over and everyone scrambled into lines. Eventually I realized they were setting up the 5-10-5 agility drill, a staple of the NFL combine and something I practiced not short of one thousand times in the past year. James and I wore cleats and sweats, but everyone else was in full pads while we cycled through the drill for a full ten minutes. We finally broke into position groups. James and I watched four other linemen go through a series of steps, following the lead of a short and stocky player who, snapping the ball, must have been the center Paul told us about. During a water break he walked over to us.

"Hey guys, I'm Brian. Nice to meet you. We're happy to have you here. Tommy, Paul says soon you will take over and coach the offensive line for practice. I'm happy to see what you can teach us. Itsa good group. We should have more guys when we get close to the game, right now it is just us."

He had olive skin, short dark hair, and a well-trimmed goatee. His bright eyes suggested a focused but kind character.

I'd been deputized as the offensive line coach, which was exciting but also made me nervous. A player and a coach are very different roles, and I wasn't sure how they'd mix. Even a player's coach [7] is never truly *one of the guys*. Would it be hard to bond with the guys if I had to yell at them too?

We had a practice plan breaking the night into five minute blocks of activity, but that seemed like a loosely defined goal, rather than something to live and die by. We made the best with what we had. At the end of practice, we trotted to the sideline for conditioning. Brian translated Niko's instructions.

"We have sprints, down and back. He says we have to be in shape. We will see who has been lazy."

Some laughs. Eyes turned towards us.

"He says we will see if the Americans came in good shape."

The Flash may be an order of magnitude smaller than any NFL team, but they sure could run. When the whistle blew, the team flew off the line, leaving James and me in the dust with two other linemen. It was all I had to finish in the middle of the pack. We ran another ten before Niko called us up, gasping for air.

I hadn't met Niko yet, but knew he was a former Flash player who had been the head coach and defensive

---

7   A coach who relates with the team, often giving them more trust and flexibility. Contrasts with an old school disciplinarian.

coordinator for a few years now. By the time he started talking, the stadium lights went out. We had a nightlight in the soft orange glow of streetlights across the tracks. Apparently the city workers that managed the stadium stayed until ten and no later.

"Good work today, but we must be better." Brian translated for us. "Look and see, the Americans are here. It is time to get serious. The season will start in a couple of weeks."

Niko looked in our direction and continued in French.

"You know you are the only ones who are paid here, and we expect a lot from you. Do not lower your level, but help us see the best way to play football. Take pride that this is your game. We expect a lot from you."

Walking off the field, a younger Arab player came up to James and me. I recognized him from the day we moved in.

"Hey do you guys need a ride back? I saw you move into Stade de Mode yesterday, I live there too. I'm Badis, [8] I'm the quarterback for the second team." He had a buoyant voice and animated smile.

"Tommy, enchante. [9] Oui that would be great, merci!"

"You want to learn French! You should watch Netflix with the subtitles. That's how I learned English. Come, my car is over here."

Walking to his car, a small coupe, he told us how he joined the Flash. Originally from Grenoble, a mountain town in the south of France near the Italian border, he moved to Paris after high school to play for the best team in France, and train under France's best quarterback – Paul Durand.

---

8 *Bad-iss*

9 *"Nice to meet you."*

"Maybe you guys don't know this, but Paul is big time! The first time I talked to him on the phone I couldn't believe it, my friends in Grenoble thought I was joking. He was the MVP of the European Championship when France defeated Germany. If anyone knows about football in France, and this is true that not many do... but *if* they do, they know Paul! So what about you guys, where are you from?"

James gave him the backstory on Long Island.

"Bro I'm from New York. Its calm, but you *gotta* try this place we got called Bubba's. This burrito they got? It's called The *Guilt* Trip. *Mad* good man, it's got friend chicken, mozzarella sticks, bacon, cheese, hot sauce and some special stuff."

"Oh my so it's true about how Americans eat! I cannot believe it! I cannot eat bacon but perhaps the rest someday!"

Driving along in the right lane, Badis slowed down to let a car turning from a side street, ahead on his right, turn in front of us.

"Why did you stop for him?" I asked.

"Is this not a rule in America? The right has the right of way unless they just come from a parking lot or small alley."

Other than this inexplicable rule, driving seemed pretty straight forward. I realized I would need to get used to roundabouts; there were no Michigan lefts [10] in La Courneuve.

Back in Stade de Mode, we settled down in the shared kitchen space and pulled a container out of the fridge. One meal per day would be provided, along with yogurt, cereal, and fresh baguettes. A group of rugby girls was in there cooking.

---

10   Instead of a left turn lane, some larger intersections in Michigan send drivers past the intersection to make a U-turn, and then a right turn. The idea is to reduce dangerous T-bone collisions.

"That is the rugby team." Badis explained. "They don't speak English and they don't do their dishes. But they are nice."

A younger guy with a shy smile joined us, clad in a grey Lacoste sweatsuit.

"Hello, I am Sotiris. You can call me Victor if this is difficult." He wasn't fluent, but certainly better than my French. "I play for the.. I don't know how to say in English." He fired off some rapid French with Badis for help, "Flag football. Yes. My mother is from Greece and my father is from Egypt."

People are endlessly interesting. With a unique worldview, personality, and set of experiences, there's always something to learn. I asked about impressions they had of other countries. Americans were the cowboys of the world. Powerful and adventurous, but ready to go it alone, with mixed results. The French were rude and culturally intimidating. A proud legacy unsure of its place in the postmodern world. The Australians – fun people but impossible to understand. The Germans – lost their honor in the twentieth century, but the ones they know are good people. Brutally unpleasant language. The Scotch had the worst English accent.

***

There's a popular video featuring Penn Jillette, an American magician, describing an encounter he had after a show with a Christian who gave him a Bible. An atheist himself, Jillette ends with a stunning claim about evangelism.

"I've always said that I don't respect people who don't proselytize. I don't respect that at all. If you believe that there's a heaven and a hell, and people could be going to hell or not getting eternal life, and you think that it's not really worth telling them this because it would make it socially awkward—and atheists who think people shouldn't proselytize and who say just leave me alone and keep your religion to yourself—how much do you have to hate somebody to not proselytize? How much do you have to hate somebody to believe everlasting life is possible and not tell them that? I mean, if I believed, beyond the shadow of a doubt, that a truck was coming at you, and you didn't believe that truck was bearing down on you, there is a certain point where I tackle you. And this is *more* important than that."

Jillette may not believe in God, but he points to something that anyone can see. If something is true, it is true for everyone, regardless of what they believe. If you are fully convinced of the veracity of a claim, and that claim has implications for everyone, it naturally follows that you ought to share how that truth will impact them. It would be selfish not to!

I am a Christian. I believe that God exists, and that he's revealed himself to the world generally through creation, and specifically in the words of the Bible. I believe that Jesus is who he says he is. While I've grown more comfortable talking about this over the years, I also enjoy being agreeable and noncontroversial whenever possible. But if I truly believe that all humans are separated from God and deserve hell because they've rebelled against him, but that through faith in Jesus' sacrifice on our behalf the relationship can be eternally restored - isn't that more important than feeling comfortable? Easier said than done.

It would be disingenuous to say I came to Paris solely to share The Gospel. [11] I want to see Europe and have a great time playing football again. However, I wouldn't be telling the full story if I didn't mention I was excited to talk about Jesus. The first opportunity

---

11 From a Greek word meaning, "the good news"

came sooner than I expected when Badis and I struck up a conversation in the hallway.

James, Badis, and I drifted into the dorm after our late dinner, James turning into his room first and Badis and I continuing on.

"Hey Badis want to have one of the *pain de chocolat* [12] I got from Carrefour?"

"It's pain *au* chocolat haha, but yes please I would!"

We walked into my room and I grabbed a box of pastries that were far more delicious than would ever be expected of a supermarket bakery. While we were eating and talking about the Flash, Badis noticed the Bible on my desk and asked,

"Are you studying something?"

"Yeah that's my Bible, I'm a Christian and try to read it every day. The notes are things that I learn about God and about what is right or that I want to do in my life."

"Wow, that's great! In France, the white Parisians say they are Christian but then they never talk about it. It is *so weird*, I don't understand! They say it is too personal. But I always hear, or at least I see in memes, that Americans are more open about God, so I guess this is true!"

While I have spent plenty of time around Americans just as shy towards spiritual conversations as any Parisian, it was an interesting observation. When we got to talking, he spoke freely and had plenty to say, talking in thoughtful soliloquies that may have gone on five minutes at a time. I was careful not to interrupt and impressed by the depth and sincerity of his faith.

Encountering a faithful Muslim who genuinely wants to follow God can be a difficult thing for a Christian. The Bible teaches very clearly that apart from faith in Jesus Christ, no one can be saved. So what to make of a devout,

---

12 A chocolate filled croissant that you'll find in any French bakery

loving Muslim? One response would be to compromise. "Perhaps the Bible isn't quite as serious as we make it out to be, maybe they *are* saved after all!" But this is no worthwhile solution. Instead of bridging a gap, it mocks the sincere claims both religions make. It would take letting go of the authority of scripture to claim salvation can be found apart from Christ. It would also patronize the Muslim, telling him that his own exclusive views aren't to be taken seriously. I think there's a better way – a loving witness. I want the discomfort I feel to drive me to show the love of Christ, and share the hope I have in him.

But we had *so much* common ground! One true God. Humans have souls. Eternal consequences of earthly decisions. Objective truth. Daily faithfulness. He shared the Teleological Argument[13] for the existence of God! Together we critiqued the prosperity gospel.[14] So when our common ground is so exciting, do I ignore the cosmic differences we have about who God is and how man can know him? Do I risk offending him to the point that our interfaith dialogue loses steam? Or trust that truth matters to him as well, and that we can handle some differences? I was asking myself these questions when he spelled out the most important difference.

"I know God will judge us all by comparing the good and bad we have done. It is all on a scale and heaven or hell depends on which way it turns. This terrifies me because I do bad things so often, from lusting over a woman to telling a lie, and I don't think I do enough good to tip it back at all. When I die, I will hope for the best."

---

13 Argues for the existence of God based on the fine-tuning of the universe.

14 A distortion of Christianity common in the United States that teaches piety will always result in health and economic prosperity

"I completely agree with you that my scale would tip towards hell, and believe that no matter how much good I've done, my offenses against the God of the universe still need to be paid for. So, the thought of standing before a holy God alone on judgement day terrifies me too. I know this is a major difference we have, but what gives me absolute confidence that I will enter heaven is that I *will* gladly claim I have no right to be there on my own, but that I have accepted Grace through Jesus' sacrifice on my behalf. I'm with *Him*."

We moved on and covered a whirlwind of topics. Politics, history, philosophy, the whole nine yards. He wondered why he was born in France with such a love for football, when there were so few opportunities here.

"I lack any great abilities or physical attributes, but I work so hard and make other people better. I just don't know if I will ever get an opportunity to show this and play in the United States. Man, that would be a dream come true!"

Eventually things wound down and Badis left my room, thanking me for the conversation, and I the same. I ought to be in bed by now but don't feel tired. Being seven hours ahead of Chicago, it's hard to shake the feeling that my friends are starting dinner when I'm trying to sleep. Tomorrow we don't have anything going on, so I'd like to get my bearings. I'll explore in concentric circles, starting with Bobigny and La Courneuve, branching out to Paris, and then eventually France and Europe.

I feel like I've gone ahead to prepare a way for my beautiful, faithful, loving wife. I want to make the mistakes now and bear their consequences so she doesn't have to. To welcome her with some semblance of competence. At very least, to have the first level of Maslow's hierarchy [15] accounted for.

---

15 Safety and physiological necessities

Thursday, January 9, 2020 – Discovery

Paul asked James and me to meet him in the office at two for a short film session, and we decided to check out the gym on our way. Fitness Park looked like an American health club, with cardio machines and a section of free weights, although the wall-sized graphics clearly emphasized the sex appeal of health beyond anything that might be deemed appropriate at home. Scantily dressed models smoldered at the camera, dripping in sweat. James rode the bike and I went through a quick leg workout. While looking for a studio room, I ended up in what I gathered was a female only section, based on the strange looks I got from a group of older ladies doing walking lunges and the loose translation of a sign on the wall.

We took the tram up to Stade Geo Andre and walked to the Flash office. Waiting for Paul, I browsed the pictures hanging in the hallway. Generations of young men wearing the Flash uniform, many of them proudly holding trophies and medals. I recognized Paul and Brian in a few of them. Then there was a shot of Ole Miss coach Mike Leach wearing a Flash jacket and bucket hat. Bruno walked out of his office and noticed me staring at it.

"Ah yes, Mike is a friend of mine, a big supporter of the Flash."

"How did that happen?"

"Oh a while back he sees a story about football in France and sends me an email. We talk and then he comes to France and spends one week with the Flash. Now we stay in touch and he comes to visit when he can."

I'm gathering that the Flash have a special place in the French football lore. Championship banners line the hall's ceiling. I ask Bruno if the Flash have always been successful.

"Oh yes since we start in 1984, we have been very good. Eleven championships is the most in Europe. We struggle last year though. After we win the French and European championships in 2018, lots of good players decide to retire, this includes Paul. But then they see how bad we are in 2019, and all decide to come back, so we can bring pride back to Flash La Courneuve."

Paul arrived shortly after, having just finished coaching a group of young quarterbacks.

"Someday, I tell you, another French quarterback will be ready to play, and we won't need to bring an American or Canadian to play. But now? these guys? So bad! Okay, let's talk about some football."

We spent an hour going through the playbook, Paul explaining the scheme, the French words we'd need to understand the call in the huddle, and lamenting the knowledge gap between French and American players.

"Most guys don't know about the Xs and Os. They just like to come and play and hit. Well, some of them do, but I just don't have time to teach everyone how to think while they play. Sometimes I get like crazy man because we keep making same mistakes! But now that you two will work with O line it will make my life easier."

He was totally open to our feedback on blocking schemes, and curious how we had run plays in the past. Thanks to extensive internet research, mostly coaching clinics on YouTube, his current ideas were largely in line with O line orthodoxy. We made suggestions and he told us what he thought was realistic to implement. Paul clearly loves the game, and was happy to have some tried and true, if not washed up, football guys to talk shop with. This was going to be a lot of fun.

***

After dinner, it was time to explore the area. I figured I'd walk into the center of La Courneuve, take a lap around the massive roundabout we'd driven through, continue on to Stade Geo Andre, and walk back on side streets. I'd be staying close to main roads and knew I could always find the clocktower of *Universite de Paris 13*, whose campus bordered Stade de Mode. Still without a phone plan, I brought a map just in case.

First I walked Northwest on N186, *Rue de Stalingrad*. Without any consistent street grid, it's hard to intuitively know which direction I'm heading. After about a mile of walking past a large hospital, a modern chain restaurant, an old church, and a smattering of small shops, N186 opened into an overwhelming flurry of activity.

This was the N186–N2 roundabout. Cars and trucks honked and swerved. Bold pedestrians crossed as they pleased. The tram bisected the intersection and commanded the right of way in three minute intervals. In the center was the tram platform with stairs down to the Paris Metro Line Seven station, 8 Mai 1945, which would be our link to the city of lights. This nod to V–E Day [16] was part of a very visible collective remembrance of World War II. For Americans, our cultural understanding of war usually focuses on brave troops heading off to fight for a just cause far away. We have a physical and psychological distance from war. But here, the old couple shuffling with walkers past the café might remember bombed out houses and the oppression of Nazi occupation.

Surrounding this roundabout was a dizzying array of restaurants, shops, and markets. On the sidewalks, street vendors sold suitcases, shoes, clothes, toys, soaps... about everything except tourist knickknacks. This was purely local. To get out of the determined foot traffic, I stepped back against a wall and stood by some smokers under an awning. In a glance I saw a bank, post office,

---

16   The date the allies defeated Nazi Germany

bakery, pizza shop, halal supermarket, Punjab takeout, kosher butcher, and some kind of casino. It was difficult to identify any sort of majority culture here. The crowd looked like an even mix of Middle Eastern, South Asian, and African, with the occasional White person.

Everything was new. The lights, smells, and sounds invigorated me. The adventure I hoped for! I could feel my mind working to take in all of the new stimuli. The observations and questions rolled in faster than I could keep up. *In Singapore they banned chewing gum downtown which was an authoritarian move that kept the streets clean, but at what cost to freedom? There's so much gum on the streets here, does that say something about the people's relationship to the government? How did all of these people groups end up here? Is this where immigrants move from former colonies? How can one town possibly support this many bakeries? Should I follow those guys across the street now or wait until the light changes? Why is everyone smoking, that hasn't been cool in decades.*

I looked at the people. Some looked busy and stressed, like they came from a tough day of work. Groups of teens walked together in packs, laughing and telling stories. Some loners strolled about, in no particular rush. Young men aggressively solicited packs of cigarettes to the crowd flowing from the trams. An older couple sat at a café. I was in a new world, but everyone else was in their most familiar element. It would be like me walking around Evanston or Grand Rapids where I have a grasp of where things are. I have context for what used to be in a spot and why there's something different now. I know the story behind the buildings and the people who live in them. But that took years of presence and engagement. I wonder what kind of familiarity I'll garner here with just seven months?

Eventually I kept moving, walking past the commotion of the roundabout towards Stade Geo Andre.

For two hours I passed through different neighborhoods, following whatever looked interesting. On Rue de Stalingrad, there were quaint three floor buildings with mortar washed brick walls and barred windows. Walls and gates protected every house and discouraged unwelcome intrusions. The architecture recalled scenes from *Band of Brothers.* [17]

Anyone who has been around me long enough has probably heard about my idea for magic time glasses. How cool would it be, I often wonder to moderately amused friends and family members, if you had a pair of glasses with a dial on the side, and you could turn the dial back to any time. Then, you would see the exact view you're looking at now, but at the moment in time you set the glasses to! Of course this isn't a realistic invention, even in the age of VR and augmented reality, but wouldn't that be so cool?? *Yes, yes Tommy that would be just as cool as the last time you brought it up.* Naysayers aside, I wished I had these glasses now. If I turned these back to May 8, 1945, might I see exhausted families spilling into the streets in celebration? What came before the buildings I can see now? What empires passed through in ages past?

GK Chesterton once said, "The world will never starve for want of wonders, but only for want of wonder." Travel lends you every opportunity to give your dose of wonder back to this amazing world.

Friday, January 10, 2020 – Ace

For breakfast, an hourlong effort left me with unpalatable eggs and a senselessly ruined pan. The eggs I'd picked up at Carrefour seemed tougher than American eggs, and after two futile cracking efforts, I threw my back

---

17   An HBO miniseries following the 101st Airborne Division through the European Theatre in World War II

into it and splattered it across the wall. The remaining eggs waited in the foolishly ungreased pan while I looked for a way to turn up the heat on the hot plate. Eventually I had a bland egg sandwich to fuel my day. Olive oil, a spatula, and a nonstick pan vaulted to the top of my list.

I set out for Carrefour, the supermarket at a nearby shopping center in Bobigny. While not a romantic Parisian street market, Carrefour was an impressive operation. The range of goods rivaled Walmart, but the produce, bakery, and butcher seemed akin to Whole Foods. I explored the massive store and gathered some provisions. There were no less than a dozen types of milk, sold by the liter. I picked one with a smiling farmer and hoped for the best.

At checkout, an older woman welcomed me, starting to scan my items, then did a double take when she looked up at a tall blond man who clearly wasn't from Bobigny.

"Bonjour monsoir, d'où êtes-vous?" [18]

"Les États Unis. J'habite ici à Bobigny, je joue au football américain pour Flash la Courneuve." [19]

DuoLingo had prepared me for this moment. Unfortunately she didn't seem to understand a thing I said. A friendly young man behind me was kind enough to step in as our translator. They exchanged some impossibly fast French dialogue.

"She says she didn't know we have American Football here but welcome. She feels bad you will see France when it is dark, cold, and we have train protests. She hopes you have a good time. She says she never sees American come to Bobigny."

I thanked them both and walked away wondering where I'd gone wrong in my French pronunciation, when a large man raced up behind, dashed through my peripherals

---

18   *"Good day sir, where are you from?"*

19   *"The United States. I live in Bobigny and I play American Football for Flash La Courneuve."*

and stopped right in front of me. It was a store clerk on roller blades.

"*Monsieur, je crois que c'est le vôtre.*" [20]

He handed me the cutting board I left at checkout and sped away to save another absent minded shopper, while I went to search for our little Peugeot in a sea of matching cars.

Back in the room, I took some time to study the playbook. We had a scrimmage tomorrow and I wanted to be as prepared as possible. Fortunately, the scheme itself was high school level complexity. Inside zone, outside zone, and power. A full line slide and man protections. Two screens, a draw, and an option run I doubt Paul ever kept it on. [21]

I would need to be self-reliant in my studying. For the past ten years, I had coaches send me scouting reports, tip sheets, film clips, and practice problems to guide my preparation. Now I had to take care of myself, and the rest of the group too.

As you move to higher levels in the United States, you encounter a remarkable number of line calls. For almost every action a lineman takes, the playbook tells you what to say. If you've been next to the same person for a while, you might come up with a handful of calls to use interchangeably, so the occasional smart defensive linemen don't catch on and cheat the play. Depending on a plethora of factors, some combination between a guard and the center could be an Ace, Single, A, Swipe, Surge, Shiv, Hawk, Drop, or Me. That's before secondary names and dummy calls.

Calls can evolve over time too. In the late third quarter playing at Nebraska, we found out, to catastrophic results, that "shiv" and "hip" sounded the same when

---

20 "*Sir, I think that is yours.*"

21 None of this makes sense to you? Not to worry, it didn't to most of our offense either.

bellowed through a mouthguard. Our center Brad and I both pulled, leaving the nose tackle free to sack Clayton, much to the delight of 90,000 Cornhuskers. Watching the film Monday, Coach Cushing demanded a new call name. With few better ideas, Brad suggested "hock," subtly referencing the loogies coach had been hocking with a cough lately, and that we had been imitating in player led film sessions. Coach thought he said "Hawk" and we went from there. All of this to say, I was surprised to see the Flash had one call for any possible combination between the guard and center, "ace." The simplicity is born out of necessity. The other guys have little training, and not much time to learn one hundred line calls with jobs and families to attend to. "Ace" would have to do for now.

James seems to be getting more comfortable around me and, thanks to endless observations and stories, I don't have to worry about awkward silences in the car or when I take a long time to finish dinner. He isn't one to let facts get in the way of a good story either.

Badis had just told us about his struggles understanding a Scottish history teacher in high school.

"Yeah my history teacher in high school was hard to understand too." James offered.

"Oh really? Like his accent?" I asked.

"Yeah he was Indian, you could barely hear him."

"I guess that could be tough in history class."

"Like sometimes he would start speaking in Indian, literally in Indian, in the middle of class."

"What the heck?"

"Yeah man thank God there was an Indian kid in class, homie would literally be translating the class for us in the back of the room."

"I guess that's good."

"Yeah but he didn't come until like halfway through the semester, so it still *sucked*!"

I'm sure there is some kernel of truth in every story. I just don't know how big it is.

Hanging out in the kitchen after dinner, Badis shared an interesting critique of American culture.

"I swear you guys have the weakest cuss words man!"

"What's that supposed to mean?!" James was incredulous, clearly proud of his colorful vocabulary.

"You just use the same five words for everything so it's the same even when you are not that mad. In France, it runs so much deeper."

"How so?" I wondered.

"We have words with complicated meanings that deliver the most destructive blow possible. One word might not just curse you, but curse your whole family or do something nasty to your dead ancestors! And Twitter brings us new words every year!"

I can confidently say I have no interest in this part of French culture.

Back in my room, I hung up a map of the world and put a new rug in place. In the orange glow of a lamp I took a breath and looked at the humble little room. I hoped Bethany would like it. I couldn't wait for her to arrive and share this experience with me. I felt like a homesteader, going ahead to prepare a safe and comfortable home before my family joined me.

Bethany has supported me for this whole ride. Instead of carrying her into a nice suburban home after our honeymoon, I carried her single suitcase into a friend's basement where we'd stay until the NFL situation sorted itself out. Our wedding gifts sat in a storage unit outside of Chicago. We'd have to wait at least another seven months before opening the flatware set and KitchenAid mixer.

Saturday, January 11, 2020 – Élancourt

The smiling farmer milk turned out to be melted ice cream. At least it tasted like it with my chocolate *Léon* cereal this morning. Paul picked us up and we set out for our joint practice in Élancourt with the Templiers, [22] a division two team in the west suburbs of Paris. We drove south from Bobigny, west along *La Périphérique*, [23] and towards Versailles. The edge of Paris is an urban jungle without any skyscrapers. The buildings were tall enough, however, to block any view of the Eifel Tower, which we hadn't seen yet.

We arrived an hour early, the first ones there and unsure how many others would show up. I grabbed the duffle bag full of jerseys from Paul's trunk and we walked into what looked like a high school. Inside, we claimed a small locker room and I started girding up my thumbs with a role of tape I'd brought from home. It had been months since I played football, and I was nervous. It wouldn't be enough to hold my own; the team was counting on me to be the best.

In the warmup lines, we mixed in with the Templiers for a dynamic stretch and another agility drill session. The others saw that James and I were Americans, and made sure we knew what to do next. In addition to our size and primitive French, the big "A" sticker on the back of our helmets has been a dead giveaway.

Practice followed a familiar script. Warmup, position group drills, seven-on-seven [24] for the skill [25] players,

22 *Templier* means *Templar*. The Knights Templar were a catholic military order established during the crusades.

23 A highway that circles Paris and defines the border between the city proper and its suburbs

24 Offense versus defense passing competition, without the linemen

25 Positions that touch the ball, aka, not the linemen

one-on-one pass protection for the linemen, a special teams period, and full team drills at the end.

Being fresh for practice can be a blessing and a curse. You aren't worn out from the season, but little nagging hurts accumulate quickly in the first days back on the field. I jammed my elbow and had a lingering soreness. In the past, I would have told an athletic trainer, who would tell me what to do. Now, I was alone. No one else would decide if I should sit out or keep going. No football player wants to take himself out of practice. It's a sign of weakness! It may be the smart thing to do at times, but it's hard to look past the machismo.

What's worse than the pain in my elbow, however, is the underlying realization that I'm not invincible, and that I came over here thinking I was. I played D-I and held my own in the NFL *(err, kind of)* doggonit! Maybe I moved on from the grind of the game and set off on a victory lap. Smooth sailing. Effortless dominance on every play. How foolish! Football will always attract warriors with pride, toughness, and ability, no matter where the field is! I had to work today. I got beat. I have turf burn. I conclusively underestimated the caliber of football I'd encounter in Europe.

Now there is quite a range. Some of these defensive linemen would get pushed back by an eighth grade double team. Others would have been solid Division III players. A couple might have cracked it in the Big-Ten. Paul told me on the drive in that the Flash had the best defensive line in Europe, and now I see why. Yuwan was a six-foot-five Olympic judo hopeful. Charles was smart and could use his hands. They called Gigi *Thanos*. I'll have my hands full every practice.

Being the American, I got everyone's best shot. I jogged to the back of the line during one-on-ones, having taken five reps in a row. Brian tapped my shoulder pads.

"They all want to go against you bro, it is how they test themselves."

James had the same deal at guard, with every interior defensive lineman lining up to see if they could prevail. I like the way James plays. With strong hands, a good base, and a knockout punch, not many made it past.

My thoughts went back to the range of players running around the field. There were eighteen and nineteen year old's, playing for fun while they went through school. This made sense. What I couldn't understand, however, was the thirty plus demographic. There's no equivalent to this in the United States. If you're playing tackle football past twenty-three years old, you are almost certainly making an obscene amount of money to do so. Sure adult softball leagues exist. The guys get together for pickup basketball. No Thanksgiving would be complete without a turkey-bowl. Some brave souls even lace up hockey skates. But you will never drive by a park and see middle aged men in full pads throwing themselves around a gridiron.

Are we so tired from all of the football we played growing up? Do we know better than to do this to our bodies? Maybe we aren't willing to strap up for free when the pipeline narrows to a few highly paid phenoms after college? Or are we forgetting something about the game that drew us to it in the first place?

Once you've been a part of a spectacle, it's hard to go back to a lower level. As the crowds get bigger and the whole ordeal seems more serious, you get used to it and can scarcely imagine going through the pain for anything less. Saturday afternoons make Friday nights seem childish, until Sundays play the trump card. But in France, you'll never know anything bigger than a Flash game, so why not ride that wave as long as you can?

Waiting for practice to end, I had a chance to meet some of the other O linemen. First I introduced myself to the loud and confident man who'd been at right tackle.

"Bonjour mon ami, quel est ton nom?" [26]

"You ask my name? My name is *big dick!*"

Duly noted.

"That's Washnee, don't mind him. He is a big liar." Brian interjected. They went back and forth, jesting in French.

We met Aadil, [27] an undersized twenty-seven-year-old computer project manager who works with Brian, Mustafa or "Moose," as everyone called him, and Sofian, a large and slow lineman who doesn't say much but seems happy to be there.

Three and a half hours after we took the field, the Templiers coach called everyone up to end practice. We broke it down and the teams split up for more speeches. At that point they decided the Americans ought to formally introduce themselves, so I stepped forward and said a prayer they'd understand me.

"Bon soir mon amis!" I said to thunderous applause. "Je suis Tommy, je suis du Les Etas Unis, et je veux aprendre la Francais. Vous sont mon freres!" [28]

They heartily approved of my haphazard effort and I was one of the guys. James gave his introduction and I led my first breakdown.

"Un, deux, trois, *CASQUE DE DIAMANT!*" [29]

After practice everyone showered and the locker room felt familiar, even if I couldn't understand the words.

---

26 *"Good day my friend, what's your name?"*

27 *Ah-deal*

28 *"Good evening my friends, I am Tommy, I am from the United States, and I want to learn French. You are my brothers!"*

29 "The Diamond Helmet" is the trophy awarded to the French league champion. In an effort to localize the game, they intentionally avoided calling it a "bowl" of any kind.

Music turned up and towel fights broke out. Moose is a character who plays the "loud, unifying, funny guy" part quite well, somehow joking with everyone in the room at once. Aadil advised me not to listen to Moose's translations unless I wanted to utter vulgar epithets at wildly inappropriate times. Afterwards I followed the crowd downstairs where, courtesy of the Templiers, we shared some warm pastries as part of a traditional French new year celebration. I was shocked to strike a chunk of plastic on my first bite, and immediately had a flimsy paper crown thrust on my head. Gigi noticed me, newly crowned and examining the plastic coin from my mouth.

"Bro, now you have good luck for 2020, that's what happens with le gâteau des rois, "the cake of kings," if you have the coin in your cake."

Afterwards we went to dinner at Steakhouse Number 5, which didn't open until seven PM, and wasn't busy until almost nine. They served an all you can eat buffet that was absolutely fantastic. For my first French meal I had a skirt steak, chicken wings, French fries, zucchini and carrots in a majestic green sauce, bowtie pasta and bacon, a sea snail, a shrimp-like crustacean, samplings from a charcuterie board, Merguez spicy sausage, vanilla and strawberry ice cream, and some interesting gummy candies. It would take a better wordsmith than me to truly describe the experience, but the flavors were deep, complex, and unique. Brian noticed my eyes rolling back while I worked on my second plate.

"You really like it, yes? This is our culture. Italy, they just have pasta and tomatoes, France is for sure the best. James why you will only eat chicken and French fries??"

"Man, I'm a picky eater, I don't really like trying all these things. The chicken be mad good tho!"

"You get that big as a picky eater? I don't understand!"

"Brrro," He leaned in, "If you saw this spot we got called Bubba's, you'd know how I got so big."

Later a linebacker with short hair and modern glasses came and sat with the linemen.

I waved to him, "Ca va?"

"What's up bro, that's good for you to practice your French, I want to practice my English too." It didn't sound like he needed much practice. "I'm Sofian, but they call me So, otherwise I get confused with big man over there."

Sofian smiled.

"What do you do for work?" I recognized him as a linebacker who played with more savviness than the young guys that just put their heads down and ran full speed ahead.

"I'm a, I'm not sure how to say it in English... a construction manager, yes. And you, why Paris? You could have picked anywhere in the world to go play this year. Why here?"

"I wanted to see a new part of the world. Paris is one of the most famous cities. And I needed a new team."

"And what did you study in University?"

"Politics and business."

"Interesting. So what will you do with this when you are done with football?"

Your guess is as good as mine, how much time do you have? I suggested something that would point him in the general direction.

"I don't know for sure yet, maybe a diplomat. I could be the ambassador to France!"

The guys raised their glasses and laughed.

Paul left early with Bruno, so James and I drove back together. We thought Mariannick programmed the car GPS to Stade de Mode, and selected *home* on the navigation screen. This GPS didn't give any context or instructions other than *turn right or take the third exit in the roundabout,* with warnings inside of a few hundred meters. Eventually we realized we weren't getting any closer to Bobigny. We ditched the GPS and charted a course East until streetlights reappeared.

Still unsure where we were, we got our answer at the top of a hill, just past an overhead bridge. A few miles in front of us, but totally unhindered, stood the Eifel Tower, beaming in its surreal yellow glow. A mighty spotlight rotated at the top, dominating the sky with an endless ray of white light. It felt like we slowed down. James and I stopped talking and took it in. We were finally in Paris.

The view was worth the detour, but after an hour and a half in the car it was time to get home. We got on La Périphérique, and followed the signs for Bobigny/ La Courneuve. Thankfully, I had James to entertain me with more astonishing stories.

"Brooo, I know all about them cheap shots, way worse than them Templars were takin. My boy used to be so dirty, he'd go after people's nuts. It was crazy."

"Ouch, that's gotta hurt."

"Like seriously man, one time at the bottom of a pile he saw this dude he hated and literally *popped* the guy's nut."

"Popped his nut?? What the heck??" I squirmed in my seat.

"Yeah bro, the ambulance had to come out on the field and everything."

I'm still fighting jetlag, but did my best to go to bed as soon as we got back. Tomorrow will be my first real trip into the city. Two of my favorite teachers from high school happen to be leading a weeklong educational trip through Western Europe, and tomorrow the tour bus rolls into Paris. I took a similar trip with them to Italy during my senior year of high school, and it had a profound impact on me. I wonder if I'd be living abroad now if it weren't for that?

Sunday, January 12, 2020 – Mona Lisa

I'd take the tram from *Hopital Avicenne* to *8 Mai 1945*, switch to the metro, and ride Line Seven into the city, where I'd meet the group at 8:45 AM in front of their hotel. The rendezvous finally happened at the Louvre, just before 2:00 PM. How was this possible? I'd propose a combination of my ineptitude and French labor relations. The tram brought me to *8 Mai 1945* just in time, but at the bottom of the stairs to the metro, I found a firmly shut gate. Walking back to street level I asked a man,

"Excuse-moi monsieur, station du métro est ouvert aujourd'hui?" [30]

"Le mouvement social! À bas avec Macron!!" [31]

I posed the same question to a less enthusiastic man who shrugged and looked back at his newspaper. *Your guess is as good as mine garcon.*

Recently, President Emmanuel Macron's government introduced a pension reform plan that would push back the retirement age. This threatened a deeply ingrained culture of work-life balance, and the strikes began.

Plan B was to drive into the city, pay for parking, and walk the rest of the way. Unfortunately, using a knockoff version of SpotHero, [32] I booked a spot for the wrong day. Stonewalled at the gate to the underground garage, I backed up, caused a scene heading the wrong way down a one way, and eventually found an expensive hour of street parking near an old church in a quiet

---

30   *"Excuse me sir, is the metro station open today?"*

31   *"The social movement! Down with Macron!"*

32   A parking reservation app

neighborhood. I walked around looking for internet and a bathroom. A skinny man with a turtle neck and snooty face seemed altogether bothered by my audacious request to use his café's WI-FI and toilet.

"No, we are not open yet. Perhaps you can read the sign. We intentionally print it in English too."

My most irrational nationalistic impulses wanted to remind him America saved their skin not once but twice from the Germans and his café was lucky it wasn't selling wiener schnitzel, but enlightened heads prevailed and I carried on my search. Twenty minutes later, I found an open café and paid for a green tea and the privilege of squeezing the lemon in their facilities. At last on a WI-FI network, I booked a new parking spot, apologized to my teacher that I'd miss the bus tour, and made plans to meet them at the Louvre later in the day.

I'd need lunch before venturing into the largest art museum in the world, and I must have ten-seconds of uninterrupted time to explain my choice: this meal was to serve a purpose - quickly sustain me until dinner, offer a bathroom, and not break the bank. If I am going to get a nice meal, I want to take my time and have it with Bethany. So yes, I went to McDonalds. Bite me.

I sat near the glass pyramid in the Louvre's courtyard, wondering if Jackie would recognize me. On my trip to Italy in 2014, Jackie was our tour guide, and awakened my curiosity for travel. She spoke seven languages, seemed at home anywhere in the world, and had a wealth of historical knowledge. On our last night in Rome, waiting in Leonardo DaVinci International Airport for a red-eye flight to Chicago, I thanked her and in my best Italian left with *arrivederci!*

She smiled but sternly corrected me, "No, *arrivederci* means goodbye. You must say, I will see you again."

Fat chance of that, I'd thought. Now those words ran through my head as I scanned the crowd. I spotted her small Filipino frame darting towards me with a smile on her face. She wasn't above saying "I told you so." We laughed and caught up with the group.

Twenty or so high schoolers stood in a rough circle, some looking around wide eyed, others glued to their phones. I smiled when I saw Mr. Brower and Mr. Davies. Social studies had always been my forte and they taught some of my favorite classes. It brought me back to the high school days I loved so much.

"Mr. Davies, it's great to see you! Thanks for the invite."

"Really glad you could join us, Tommy. By the way, you're like twenty-four now call me Seth."

Mr. Davies (or should I say, Seth), spent the previous two years teaching at an international school in Jakarta, and was glad I'd taken the plunge and moved overseas.

"How long was it before it felt like home? Before you were really comfortable there?" I asked as we made our way through the security line.

"It never felt like home, I don't think it could. But eight months is about when it felt familiar."

That would be right about the time we had to leave, so I guess this would be an adventure up until the end.

What started as a royal palace in the twelfth-century made the transition to museum when Louis XIV opted for Versailles, but left his art collection in the Louvre. With over seventy-thousand square feet of display space, we wouldn't be seeing everything.

"My friends you must make a plan for what you will see today," Jackie warned the group, "if you spent ten seconds looking at each piece for eight hours every day, it would take you six months to see it all. And my friends you must look at *Mona Lisa* for more than ten seconds."

DaVinci's masterpiece would be our first stop. We walked into a massive gallery that housed just this one painting. Despite being warned a dozen times how small *Mona Lisa* is, I was still shocked when I saw it. It looked like a postcard in the distance, but this thirty-by-twenty inch oil might go for as high as one *billion* dollars if it ever hit the auction. An international crowd snaked back and forth, oozing towards their moment at the front. Selfie sticks poked above the crowd like lighters at a concert.

When I took AP European History, Mr. Brower was especially interested in the role art played in shaping and reflecting culture. As questions popped into my head, I didn't have to scour Google; I could just ask him.

"Maybe I shouldn't say this out loud, but what exactly makes Mona Lisa so special?" I asked, looking into her enigmatic eyes.

"You're not the only one to wonder that." He replied, craning forward for a better view than his 6'7" Dutch frame already gave him. "DaVinci used forward thinking techniques, layering the background, and executed the mechanics flawlessly. But more than that, it's probably the mystery of it all. Who is she? What's she thinking? The intrigue of DaVinci himself is wrapped up in her eyes."

We moved on through the halls, where the scale and beauty of the art was overwhelming. My favorite paintings, however, were down the road in Musée d'Orsay, home of the impressionists. I turned to Mr. Brower again while we looked at a war scene with photographic detail.

"So how'd we get from these vivid realistic paintings to impressionism?"

"Well, capturing the exact details with paint became less of an achievement when a camera came along that could outdo anyone with the push of a button. So what art could uniquely do, was capture the feeling. The emotion of the moment."

When our time was up, we packed into vans and drove to dinner. It seemed strange to be sitting at the adult table, watching the excited students recount the day. As much fun as I had back then, I felt at peace on the other side. When I was in Italy, I remember talking with a freshman who was looking forward to the rest of high school with some nervous anticipation.

"Know right now that you'll get to your senior year and say time flew by," I told him, "so give that up, loosen your grip on time and enjoy what you can in each moment. Then when you have to move on, you won't be surprised or feel cheated. You'll be ready for it."

I'm sure it wasn't as eloquent, but that was the flashback while I enjoyed a flat bread pizza and chatted with my former teachers. It doesn't seem that long ago I was at the other table, but then again, a lot can happen in six years. The seniors talked about their college plans, some with excitement, others dreadful uncertainty. I hoped they knew life would move on if things didn't go exactly like they expected.

The last stop of the night would be a trip up the Eifel Tower. Pulling up to the glowing structure I'd seen from a distance the night before, I heard Thomas Rhett singing in the back of my head, *If I never get to see the northern lights, if I never see the Eifel Tower at night...* Cheesy, yes, but it felt special. Countless bolts and beams were illuminated, stitched together long before 3D computer models and tower cranes. There was no precedent for such a structure in 1887. The theoretical limits of iron were tested in a grand and wild experiment.

The up-lit open lattice reminded me of a wooden roller coaster, but with the scale of a skyscraper. We took a rickety cable car to the top and watched the city of lights spread out beneath us. If only Bethany were here.

Jackie points out the landmarks below, as we look down in the crisp January air. Above us, the spotlight makes its rounds over the city, beaming a little bit of magic into the night sky.

These profound thoughts were interrupted by two juniors, one of whom I'm told was Tik Tok famous.

"Umm, hi. You play, *football*, right? Is it like, famous around here? We're making a dance video and wonder if you should be in it. It could, like, help us get some extra views."

"I won't lie to you, not at all. My dancing on the other hand, that could be what you're looking for."

"Ummm, yeah we'll see about that. You know the *clambroflihoopachacha bop*, right?" You can insert any gibberish there, I had no clue. They read my blank face.

"Ok probably not, but umm, I guess you can still be in it if you want."

No one can blame my dancing problems on inhibitions or lack of passion, but I'm sure the poor girl lost followers after this episode. I conclusively belonged at the uncool adult table.

Monday, January 13, 2020 – Low Turnout

The practice script was set and I was ready for my first real test as a coach. I planned out a series of drills – run focus for the first twenty-minute block of individual, pass for the latter. I racked my brain for the most useful drills I went through in college and the NFL. Punch timing. Double teams. Kick and drag. It was all there, printed on a script Paul handed me on the way out of our film session.

I rolled out of the locker room in full pads at 7:00 PM, with plenty of time to set up before the 7:30 warmup. I collected some bags and footballs, brought them to our area in the northeast corner, and started stretching. By around 7:45, the quarterbacks and receivers were throwing a ball around, but other than James and me, there were no linemen in sight, not even at 8:00, when we finally started the warmup. The breakdown came and went, everyone scrambled off to their position area for individual drills, and James and I looked at each other.

"Well, I guess it's just us!" I sighed.

"Yeah doesn't look like these homies are gonna make it today. I remember Brian saying that cuz' he coaches the kids team, he's got stuff with the Flash every night of the week, so he just stays home on Mondays."

I couldn't blame him. What other extracurricular demands that kind of time? Football isn't just a thing you do in your free time, it's a lifestyle, a grand campaign you embark on every fall that asks for everything you've got. At least if you want to do it well. The others had jobs and families, so a Monday night practice two weeks away from any game wasn't at the top of the to do list.

James and I walked through the drills I planned, compared what we've learned, and worked on our pass sets. It's amazing how much you can get out of some focused time by yourself on a field. I locked in and visualized the defense. *Inside zone right. Left. Outside zone, power. Wide DE speed rush, inside move, bull rush. Skip pull, cut the backer.*

After an hour in our own little world, Michel, the defensive line coach, invited us over for one-on-ones. Since practice was winding down, there were only two of us, and everyone was getting cold, I figured this would be an NFL tempo drill, if not half speed. While different coaches do things differently, NFL tempo typically means you come off fast and shut it down at first contact. Keep everyone off the ground. Instead, I got knocked back by a full speed bull rush, with no whistle to call the dogs off. On my heels, I felt myself back right into the quarterback, an older D lineman standing in to catch the snap. *Dang it.* You should always err to going harder. It's easier to tone it down if you went too hard than to pick up the pieces of your ego after someone else decided to play faster than you.

So it went on, the D line taking turns pushing on James and me. Our defensive ends play extremely tight, lining up just a shade wider than head up on me. Some American ends can be two or three yards outside of the tackle, forcing him to kick back at warp speed, or at least as close to that as a three hundred pound man can move. The Flash, however, seemed dead set on the inside move. Twice I overset the end, kicking too wide and giving him an open door to the quarterback. Eventually I took a small step and stayed put, forcing them to run through me or go outside.

My presuppositions were failing me. As long as I've played football, the defensive end has had to contain the edge. Nothing gets outside! At higher levels, there are exceptions to this rule, but the defense offers clues that someone else has the edge. None of this mattered tonight. They wanted to go inside, and I had to learn how to compete in La Courneuve.

Walking into practice, I was ready to have fun and be friends with everyone. I can still see a place for that, but I need to fan the flame in my heart and bring some intensity back to my game. Getting walked back into the quarterback threw some coals on. The next time I lined up against the skinny ball of fire who pushed me after the whistle, I jump set him, smacked his helmet, swiped his hand off my chest, and drove my shoulder into his back on the ground. *Ugh.* Football rage was back. While they wouldn't respect me if I slacked off, there was a fine line between intensity and taking cheap shots.

Back in my room, a flood of emails remind me that the technicalities of life don't pause just because you've gone off to live a temporary fairy tale in Paris. Bethany was navigating a numbingly slow bureaucracy to apply for an Army medical school scholarship, and we'd need a place to live when we moved to Tennessee. We could rent a three bedroom apartment for the price of a studio in Chicago, but I'd rather think about football than throwing more money down the drain in rent.

Before bed, I started reading *Soccer Empire*, by Laurent Dubois. Dubois asks fascinating questions about sports and multiculturalism. In the World Cup, why do Caribbean and African citizens usually root for Brazil against European countries? What does it mean that France's team is a collection of immigrants from former colonies? He argues that sports condense and propel larger political debates. Many of my teammates are from former French colonies around the world. Saint-Denis is discussed at length in the book. I feel like I'm living in this story.

Tuesday, January 14, 2020 - Doukie

I kicked things off this morning with poultry redemption in the kitchen. Some olive oil, the right hot plate, a spatula, seasonings, and Merguez sausage totally changed the game, and I enjoyed a fine breakfast.

Eight offensive linemen were ready by the time individual drills started. We ran through the script and things went smoothly. At one point, a chubby man with a thick red beard walked up to our drill and started talking with the group. Moose was thrilled to see him, and eagerly walked away from his post on defense to chat it up. Sofian meandered over to join them. While Moose wanted to introduce me to his friend, Brian exhorted me to keep practice moving.

"Come on man, you have to be hard on them. Make the drill continue, we have to be much better. Let's go."

After a few full team plays, we hit the line for conditioning. At 10:00 the lights shut off, but Niko kept pushing us under the orange glow of the streetlight. Further north than any point in the continental United States, Paris is a dark place in January; the sun gets low in the sky before 4:00 PM.

A cold breeze turns into a frigid wind as we step up for another gasser. My lungs are sucking in freezing air, my heart beats out of my chest, and my legs ache. But it's exhilarating. Our squad is pushing through it, together. I'm loving it so much, I can't help but add something to this energy.

"Bon Sofian, bon! Très rapid Washnee, je aime! Oui oui oui!!" [33]

Washnee smiled and shook his head through labored breaths, I think they get the point.

Niko finally blew the whistle, but instead of heading to the center, the team congregated on the sideline and started a slow jog around the field. The linemen moved to the front, and the rest of the team fell in behind. Sofian led the pack. After we passed the first goal post, I heard Doukie, a tall and lean wide receiver, holler,

"Deux pour moi et quatre pour toi!" [34]

He started clapping out a rhythm.

Clap clap-clap-clap clap clap

Clap clap-clap-clap clap clap

For a second, all I heard was cleats tapping the turf, and then thunder broke out.

CLAP CLAP-CLAP-CLAP CLAP CLAP

CLAP CLAP-CLAP-CLAP CLAP CLAP

CLAP CLAP-CLAP-CLAP CLAP CLAP

CLAP CLAP-CLAP-CLAP CLAP CLAP

I had chills as we finished the lap and finally brought it together around Niko. A beam of light sweep through the sky from the south. Wondering if there

---

33 *"Good Sofian good! Very fast Washnee, I love! Yes yes yes!"*

34 *"Two for me and four for you!"*

was a movie premier or night club nearby, I suddenly remembered the spotlight watching over Paris from the Eifel Tower. Thirty seconds later, it made another pass.

Paul translated while Niko went on about how sloppy the practice was. I had zoned out counting the spotlight's intervals when a voice broke out from the back of the huddle. It took me a minute to figure out what was happening, but Doukie was shouting at Niko! I couldn't believe it; there's really no frame of reference for something like this, coming from a stable American program. The coach is the unquestioned leader, especially in public. Americans learn not to even break eye contact while the coach talks after practice, much less publicly challenge him! Paul had been translating for me until the back and forth ensued, and he put his face in his palm. Eventually it died down and we put our hands together for the breakdown.

Un, deux, trois, Flash! Un, deux, trois, Flash! Un, deux, trois, Flash! ooO Flash!

"What was that all about?" I asked Paul while we jogged off the field.

Paul sighed, "Uhhh man I don't really know, Doukie is upset with Niko for last year. He blames him for the bad season last year, he says we have to be better now. He wants Niko to be better too I think."

I was torn. At first it seemed blatantly disrespectful, but could it be an equally amazing act of loyalty and commitment to the team?

In the locker room after practice, changing and getting out takes twice as long as it should, for a peculiar reason. Every single person says goodbye to everyone else individually. I was unstrapping my ankle braces and looked up to see a line patiently waiting for me in the unheated locker room.

"Salut!" [35]

---

35 "Bye!"

"Bonne soirée!" [36]

"À bientôt!" [37]

"Au revoir, mon ami!" [38]

A handshake with each one. It wasn't just special treatment for the Americans, they made their way around the room. How wonderfully inconvenient.

Driving back, Badis lamented the state of the Divison II team, which practices on an adjacent field.

"It is so frustrating man! So many guys just come for fun and they don't really care. I move from Grenoble so I can play with the Flash and just waste my time each night!"

James offered some curses on the D-II team for solidarity, and I felt for him. I'm sure he'd kill for a shot on a high school team in the states, but he's an ocean away from that opportunity.

Back in Stade de Mode's kitchen, James and I relived some of our high school glory days. Badis and Sotiris couldn't believe it.

"You tell me Friday Night Lights is very real? To play for school? With cheerleaders and bands?"

"And the quarterback is really popular in the whole school? Oh man I wish I could do this! Even just to play football after school with my classmates, this is so *cool!*"

"Yeah I guess it is pretty cool, do people from France ever go to the US for football?" I asked.

"Sometime but it is very rare. If you get sent to boarding school you can do this, or you must find a junior-college to give you opportunity."

---

36   *"Good night!"*

37   *"See you soon!"*

38   *"Goodbye, my friend!"*

"That's what I'm talking about homie, that'd be mad cool if you came over." James said, taking a bite of his pasta.

"Yes, I even found on YouTube that I should have a schedule for my training."

He showed us a draft of his plan, with two workouts, film sessions, stretching, and six hours of sleep. He seemed relieved when I told him about the recent emphasis on sleep in US football circles.

"Well, maybe I will take out the early stretching session then. But I can put it after I am home from work."

Wednesday, January 15, 2020 – Baunderie

With practices on Monday, Tuesday, and Thursday nights, Wednesday is totally free. In what has become a typical morning, I started off reading my Bible, making a quick breakfast, running to Fitness Park for a workout, and coming back to spend a few hours reading and practicing French. Practicing with teammates has a higher yield than DuoLingo, but at the same time, I need to be careful who I trust. Ever the joker despite being a thirty-five year old father, Moose is inclined to give the most vulgar translation possible. Had I listened to him last night when I wanted to compliment a receiver on his speed, I would have looked him in the eye and told him to *eat my balls!* Who's to say how many times I've been duped.

Laundry here is turning out to be quite a bother. We have one washer and one dryer in a dorm with fifteen or so athletes. Since I got to college, I've put my workout clothes on a loop and dropped it in the bin, confident it would be in my locker the next morning. Now, it's war. I constantly check the *buanderie* for an open machine and pounce on every opportunity for a clean pair of shorts. Walking into the dorm after my lift this morning, I checked the machine, saw an opening, and jogged to my room at the end of the hall. As fast as I could, I grabbed the laundry bag and hustled back out, laughing at myself for the urgency when the hall was clearly empty. Victoriously I swung the door open only to see James shut the machine and turn around with a grin on his face. Touché.

If I might present one more complaint, I'm thankful for the private pantry closet they set aside for the Americans, but found out today that we'd be sharing it with an eight legged demon. I have never seen such a big spider, and shudder to even think back on it. Bethany slanders my good name by saying I'm afraid of spiders. I just prefer they stay in their place, far away from me. I tried humanizing him, to mixed results. Fredrich is a kind old French arachnid who takes pride in protecting his American friends from undesirable bugs.

With a working grasp of La Courneuve and Bobigny, it was time to venture into Paris via public transit. Line Seven brought me to *Chatelet*, a sprawling metro station with fruit markets and moving walkways, and I walked upstairs to find the Paris you might dream of. It rained earlier, and now twinkling lights reflected off the pavement. Classy cafés and bistros lined the streets. The roads were packed with bustling, fashionable people. What they say about fashion in Paris is true.

Most everyone was making a real effort to look good. Men wore pea coats, a scarf, tailored pants, and leather boots. Even after six months of marriage and a childhood with two sisters, I lack, in a strictly literal sense, the vocabulary to describe what the women sported. But it was bona fide, if not a bit edgier than Sunday best.

I walked a few blocks to the Seine, [39] crossed it on a bridge built by Napoleon, and walked up to Notre Dame. The storied church was recently ravaged by a fire that severely compromised its structural integrity.

---

39 The river that runs through the heart of Paris

With the enthusiastic support of the French government and people, restoration was underway. Thankfully, the famous front facade was intact, so I joined a small crowd admiring it from behind a tall construction fence.

Built between 1163 and 1345, this thing has been around for a while. A perfect opportunity to whip out the magic time glasses! I imagined myself around the time of the American Revolution, standing next to Ambassador Thomas Jefferson, listening to him admire the still six-*hundred* year old structure. I could no easier imagine what the world was like when Notre Dame was built than what it would be like today without it. This led me to lament the uninspiring lifespan of the great structures built in modern times. In 1975, the Pontiac Silverdome opened to the marvel of the sports world. A colossal achievement! The pride of Michigan! Yet by 2002, the dome was an eyesore that had been replaced by Ford Field. Notre Dame has been around more than thirty times as long as the Silverdome lived, but the world is still scrambling to save it.

A police car speeding along behind me broke this trance, but put me back into a new one. American police sirens are a cacophony of electrical sounds, but every siren here was a flat, two toned pattern. Why? I stood in the Parisian night with a hand on my chin for no short time, came up with nothing, shrugged and moved along. Without a phone plan and the world's information in my pocket, I'm forced to think about questions myself before seeing what other have to say.

Back in the metro station, I noticed the advertisements lining the walls. Advertising draws heavily from psychology, presenting goods and services as the antidote to people's deep-seated needs and insecurities. I couldn't read many of the slogans, but the images were more serious and sexy than ads you'd see in America. Think perfume commercials to sell macaroni.

The metro system was similar to others I have been on. I assume they share best practices at metro system conventions, along with themed drinks and gripes about belligerent passengers. An automated turnstile where you tap a card, numbered or colored lines with endpoints indicating the direction of travel. Transfers within stations to other lines. The cars seemed slightly newer than Chicago trains, but nothing like the futuristic Tokyo transit system. While I was on high alert trying to learn the system, others were just going about their lives. This was their grind, their routine.

Bethany arrives tomorrow morning at 9:40 AM, CDG Terminal 1. The public service unions, which include the man who unlocks Stade Geo Andre, organized a planned day of strikes, so practice is already canceled. A full day to welcome my bride to the city of love!

Landing in Frankfurt en route to Paris with my expensively overweight bags.

A very large museum with a surprisingly small Mona Lisa.

CHAPTER II

Bethany Arrives

Thursday, January 16, 2020 - Bethany

I woke up with the excitement usually reserved for Christmas morning, ready to see Bethany again. It felt like we got away with something, moving to Paris. As if the powers that be would soon realize two newlyweds weren't supposed to be traipsing around Europe. We'd be sent back to the Midwest for a nine-to-five at once!

My dream of competently welcoming Bethany to Paris nearly ended before she landed, when I couldn't find a gas station that accepted my cards and almost ran out of fuel on A1. [1] Thankfully, a station near the airport was more than happy to rob me and send me on my way. As an American, I expect gas and driving to be very affordable, just a minor inconvenience. This morning I got twenty-six liters, about half a tank, for €40. Some quick math [2] put that at $6.5 per gallon! Europeans

---

1 The Highway to the airport

2 (3.785L=1Gallon, \$1.11=€1) -> [40/{26.5/3.785}]*1.11 = 6.5)

may expect more public services, but they certainly pay for it.

I parked in the Terminal 1 short term lot and rushed to the arrivals gate. I stood on my tiptoes, trying to spot her in the flow of tired passengers streaming out. A minute later, there she was! She looked tired, but excited. Maybe a little nervous, clutching her two bags and looking up around the cavernous terminal. She was wearing a green hat she'd knit herself last year. I could tell she curled her brown hair before leaving. I felt a rush of emotion. She was beautiful.

I waved and she spotted me! She smiled and shuffled over for a long awaited hug. I couldn't help but (at which point I'm often reminded that yes, yes you *can* help it) break into a "reunited and it feels, so good!" rendition with a shameless stupid grin. We're back!

Driving home, and I feel comfortable calling it home now that Bethany will be with me, I showed her some of the neighborhood before heading to Stade de Mode Chambre 12 for the grand tour! A queen but never high maintenance, Bethany saw our humble little room and told me, "it's perfect."

I brought her up to speed on how things had been going until she drifted off in an understandable wave of jet lag. She slept a while and then we went on a basic tour of Bobigny. We shared a croissant and two macarons at a bakery near Carrefour, then walked towards the *8 Mai 1945* roundabout. Bethany gazed around, taking it in, just as I had a week earlier.

Now it was time to show off my French. Walking past a flower shop, I gave Bethany a smug look and turned to the owner.

"Excusez-moi monsieur, ces plantes sont bonnes pour l'intérieur de la maison?" [3]

---

3   *"Excuse me sir, are these plants good for inside the house?"* At least, that was the hope.

A newsboy cap and a blank stare.

"Really connecting with the locals, I see." Bethany taunted.

Remedial language simplifies you. If you only have the vocabulary of a second grader, that's about the ceiling for your communication. I think of how I subconsciously react to people who don't speak English very well. *They must be simple. Their burdens, passions, and insights are less than yours.* Language lays down tracks for our humanity to run on – may we never confuse limited tracks with limited humanity!

Back in the kitchen after our walk, I introduced Bethany to James, Badis, and Sotiris, who were hanging out at the table.

"Bethany! We have been excited to see you! Welcome to France!" Badis said as he shook her hand.

"Yes hi, I am Sotiris, you can call me Victor if Sotiris is difficult, it is name of Greece."

"What's up, I'm James, glad you made it."

I wonder how Bethany's arrival will change the social dynamic. We were the four amigos of Stade de Mode! Thankfully, Bethany has social grace and can fit in anywhere; I can already tell people like having her around. We want to make friends, but at the same time, to be together as much as possible. On a honeymoon, it wouldn't be right to spend all of your time in a group. The honeymoon ended in Jamaica, but we are still newlyweds.

Friday, January 17, 2020 – Almost Missed It

Today began later than expected, seven minutes later to be precise. I was supposed to wake up at 8:30 AM, read, make breakfast, and then leave to drop Badis off at Gare d'Est. [4] We'd be on the road at 10:00 sharp. Badis

---

4 Paris East Train Station

was invited to a German football combine this weekend, and his former teammates were throwing him a birthday party afterwards. [5] He spent some of the little he makes waiting tables for a train ticket to Cologne with a layover in Strasburg.

I woke up at 10:04, rushed out, and we were in the car by 10:07. ETA: 10:47. Without traffic, this would have taken us twenty-minutes. We sat in absurdly slow traffic and watched the ETA tick back. Motorcycles raced by in the tight lanes between stalled cars. His train left at 11:00, and it wasn't long before the ETA read 11:04. We stopped talking much other than to occasionally curse an idling bus or slow driver.

I was thinking of the contingencies and they weren't good. This was a non-refundable ticket and the only train today.

"Maybe I could drive you to Strasburg to catch the second train?"

"Thanks bro but these trains go so fast, you would be three hours late if we left now."

I saw the gravity of my tardiness setting in. He'd miss an important football opportunity and a birthday party. As we got closer, Badis told me the train actually left at 11:09 and there was minimal security to go through. A flicker of hope! To Badis' delight, I veered into the oncoming lane to pass a slow moving truck and zipped through an orange light.

"Let's go! You drive like a real Parisian now!"

At 11:04, we pulled up to another clog of standstill traffic, but were only two hundred meters from the station.

"Hop on out here, you can make it! My phone doesn't work but I'll wait in front for a minute if you don't!"

---

5 Badis played last season with a Division II team in Germany

"Thanks bro!" Badis slammed the door and tapped the hood as he hurdled a fence and made a run for it.

Godspeed my friend.

I ended up driving the wrong way on another one way – a bike lane, this time. Now wasn't the time to act like a savvy Parisian, so I rolled down the windows and played the *harmless but totally lost and confused American* act as well as I could. I got laughs and shaking heads instead of an angry mob, and found a spot to idle in front of a post office, which also dished out free WI-FI. I rushed to WhatsApp for an update.

Tommy it was very close but I made it!

Whew.

After a late lunch, the shadows grew long and a breeze picked up. Bethany would see the Eifel Tower tonight! Walking towards the tram, we passed by Stade de Mode's small office building where Pascal, the facility manager, lived. Figuring it couldn't hurt to introduce ourselves, we knocked on the door, expecting to say hello and be on our way. Out stepped a squat old man with thick glasses, a blue striped sweater, and a curious look on his face. He rattled off some French, read our blank faces, and fished a phone out of his pocket. He hummed while he navigated through the apps with one calloused finger until he found a web browser, typed in a URL, and seemed pleased that Google Translate popped up. He held it close to his mouth and spoke very deliberately, then a second later the female computer voice provided a translation.

"My name is Pascal. You must be the Americans. Welcome. Come inside please for coffee now."

We obliged, sat down, and talked back and forth through his phone. The system worked well enough that I wondered how long it would be before learning languages went out of style. He told us about birds around Paris, his thirty-eight year tenure at Stade de Mode, and his upcoming retirement, which would mean more time with grandchildren. As a political science student, I couldn't help but ask his thoughts on Macron.

"Macron is the worst president in the history of France. He is a former banker who just wants to enrich himself. We should bring back the Franc, gas prices are too high. The government is bull****," the computerized woman candidly informed us.

Eventually we asked the phone to thank him for the hospitality and went on our way. Dressed in the best dressy casual we could muster, we set off into the city. Transferring from Line Seven to Nine at *Chaussé d'Antin Lafayette*, we got off at *Franklin D Roosevelt* and walked up the stairs to behold *Champs Elysees*, one of the great avenues of the world. At the end of the road was the Arc de Triomphe. On the way, we passed designer outlets, street performers, and Michelin rated restaurants. It was like the Magnificent Mile, Fifth Avenue, and Monroe Mall, [6] all leading to a D.C. monument.

The Arc de Triomphe was more spectacular than I expected. Inaugurated in 1836, the arch honors soldiers that fought and died during the Napoleonic Wars and the French Revolution. It stands sixty-meters tall and forty-five wide, covered top to bottom in dramatic sculpting. So many movies and pictures have taken me here in the past. Cars, busses, and motorcycles raced through the encircling roundabout like minnows while the monument stood steadfast in the center. [7] Thankfully we didn't need

---

6   A globally significant avenue in Grand Rapids, Michigan. You haven't heard of it? Hmm. I must say that's embarrassingly uncultured of you

7   Any accidents occurring within the roundabout are handled on a "no fault" basis, wherein the respective insurers split the cost 50/50 instead of trying to identify and assign blame, the only such zone in Paris. Apparently police and insurance companies had given up hope of sorting out the messes that arose in such a whirlwind

to cross this madness, but took a pedestrian underpass to the base.

We were going to take a quick look at the Arch from underneath and head home, but this plan took a delightful twist when we noticed a group of Americans standing by the staircase, lining up to go to street level. They were mostly well dressed middle-aged and older men wearing green VFW[8] side caps. An old man at the front carried an American flag. After standing awkwardly against the wall looking at them, I walked over to investigate. I found one who wasn't already talking to someone else.

"Hi I'm Tommy, my wife and I are Americans. Are you guys here for a ceremony or something?"

"Tommy I'm John, pleased to meet you. Welcome to the city. We're vets with the Benjamin Franklin VFW post, so we all live in Paris. Today's old Ben's birthday, so we're joining the French military for their nightly ceremony. You're welcome to join us."

Before we could talk about it, the old man called out and we were marching in line with the vets and their families, heading upstairs and then standing at attention while a crowd looked on from outside the roped off area. Underneath the arch, France has a tomb for the unknown soldier, placed here in 1919 and complete with an eternal flame. This was akin to Arlington's changing of the guard ceremony.

Waiting for the ceremony to start, Bethany noticed another out of place young couple behind us.

"Hi!" She called in a hushed tone. "Do you two live here too?"

"No, we were looking at the group of Americans and saw you two join, so we tagged along!"

"Nice! What brings you to Paris?"

"We're on our honeymoon!"

"Aw congrats! Where are you from?"

---

8 Veterans of Foreign Wars

"We're from a city in West Michigan, Grand Rapids."

My ears perked up. *What??* I joined in.

"No way! I'm from Grand Rapids too!"

"Stop it! What high school did you go to?"

"Grand Rapids Christian, go eagles. Where do you guys live?"

The guy laughed and looked at his wife.

"Since you're a local, you probably know about the castle in Grandville. That's us."

Ha! The Grand Castle was either a charming feat of architectural imagination or a gimmicky eyesore, depending on whom you ask. Since I'm not a good cynic, I'll cast my lot with the former. Modeled after the Neuschwanstein Castle in Germany, it was actually the second largest castle structure in the world. I will admit the old world's castles are markedly more elegant.

It was time for the ceremony to start. The wind picked up to a howl and rain started attacking our flanks, but the French and American veterans stood at attention together while French children laid a wreath near the flame. Accompanied by a drum and bugle, the crowd began to sing *La Marseillaise*.[9] It was a touching display of unity and strength. The veterans of two of the world's great republics honoring those who fell in the defense of their shared values. I thought of pictures of the Nazi army marching underneath the arc, the epitome of tyranny and oppression. What a contrast from the honor and beauty on display before us! Bethany squeezed my hand and smiled, she could tell I was eating this up.

Afterwards, the vets invited the honeymoon couple and us to join them for drinks. I followed their lead and ordered a *Kier*, a white wine blend I'm told is a Parisian thing. The vets insisted on covering the tab, since we were

---

9 The French national anthem

their guests. What generosity with their time, resources, and fellowship!

Everyone was amused by our story.

"Wait, you don't mean soccer, right? We're talking *real* football?" The man from the front of the line, a Vietnam Army vet asked.

"Well how about that, we can finally watch some live football again! Here's my card, I want you to email me your schedule. I'll send it over to the embassy too, I know a lot of expats will be interested." He was a naval officer during Desert Storm and worked here for the OECD. [10] We continued on, learning about their experiences and what drew them to Paris. I posed a question I'd been considering.

"So what do the French actually think about Americans? Do they like us? Hate us? Something in between?"

The others looked around to see who would answer and then turned to the Vietnam vet at the end of the table who leaned forward in his chair.

"I'll tell you what, I moved here after Nam and haven't left. This is just what I think. The British like us on the surface, but not underneath. Like the younger brother that grew up to be richer than them. In France, they might scoff at us, but deep down there's a respect. They were our first ally and we came twice in their time of need. They haven't forgotten that, nor will they any time soon." He leaned back and took a sip of his drink. "But that's just what *I* think."

I thought of Churchill's line, declaring that they would continue to fight (yes, on the beaches), "Until, in God's good time, the New World, with all its power and might, steps forth to the rescue and liberation of the old." It felt like we were heirs to a grand story.

---

10 Organization for Economic Cooperation and Development, an intergovernmental consortium of mostly rich countries that promotes free trade and democracy

I thought of a line from *Midnight in Paris*, where Adriana exclaims, "That Paris exists and anyone could choose to live anywhere else in the world will always be a mystery to me." I wouldn't go that far, but did feel some of the magic of the city.

After parting ways with our new friends, we walked to the Eifel Tower. What a beautiful sight! Having Bethany around makes everything better. We took the elevator to the second deck and marveled at the view of the city and the rest of the tower, even taking advantage of the WI-FI to Facetime each of our parents.

Back in our kitchen, we sat down for a 1:00 AM dinner of cod, potatoes, onion, and tomato. Trying to find our way back from the city, Bethany was gracious and easygoing when the first two metro stations were closed for *Le mouvement social*. It reminded me again why I wanted to marry her so badly. Finally walking back to our room, a light caught my eye. We looked south and I noticed, just a half inch tall from our perspective, the lights of the Eifel Tower. Lest we forget where we are.

Saturday, January 18, 2020 – Versailles

The *Chateau de Versailles* was a royal residence that began as a hunting lodge but became the center for all operations under Louis XIV, the Sun King, who was suspicious of the anti-monarchial winds blowing in Paris. An article I read supposed the entire property was worth $50 billion on the market, but you won't find it on Zillow. The scale and attention to detail are remarkable. Nearly every surface was covered in gilded wood carvings, colored marble, or paintings commissioned by legendary artists.

We took an audio-guided tour of the palace, with plans to spend a day perusing the equally legendary gardens come spring. There was a lot to take in. Every detail was designed to inspire awe and fear of the French crown. The paintings postured the king as a godlike defender of an eternal kingdom. As a Christian, I can safely say that monarchy is my favorite form of government – with an important catch. The monarch must be the eternal God of the universe. Absent this, I want nothing to do with monarchy. A republic will be just fine. That being said, it was fascinating to learn about some of history's most powerful kings and the lives they lived here. In one particularly odd audio lesson, we learned about the *Levee* ceremony, wherein the king would wake up and get dressed in the presence of as many as one-hundred nobles and courtly staff. Those early lobbyists fortunate enough to be nearby while he put on his wig could make their petitions.

A highlight was the famous Hall of Mirrors, the high water mark of opulent monarchy. Delegations from around the world were led through this show of wealth and force before entering the king's chambers. Mirrors were a special luxury at the time, and the walls are lined with them, reflecting the sun or the chandeliers coming from the ceiling.

After completing our walk through the palace, we strolled the barren, but still immaculate gardens. The rows of gravel paths between perfectly kept hedges never ended. We'd walk for a while, come across an exquisite fountain, and pick a new direction to head off in. I'm sure if I turned my time glasses back to the revolution, this wouldn't be so peaceful. The audio guide described a bleak day in 1789 when five-thousand angry Parisians stormed the palace and put an abrupt and violent end to courtly life.

On the way back to the car, a casual restaurant caught my attention. Buffalo Grill's red sign sported longhorns – an American themed restaurant! The

United States excels in picking up a national cuisine and repackaging it for our own consumers. I have wondered, does anyone do this to us? Here, that's exactly what they were going for, and while the U.S. has a number of distinct cuisines, they went with country western. The menu was composed of various barbecue dishes, the décor frontier scenes. Cowboys and cattle. Mountains and valleys. George Strait sang a sad song inside. Someone thought this was worth capturing and sharing with another part of the world.

Sunday, January 19, 2020 – Ikea

After a trip to the discount hygge wonderland that is Ikea, we finished furnishing our pad with an area rug and throw pillow. Living large. We even pinned a string of lights above the bed. It feels like our honeymoon, having this much time together. Unfortunately we haven't outgrown some of the problems we discovered early in marriage.

"How can it possibly take you this long to finish eating? I'm not even eating fast and finished before you got halfway."

"Now that I'm not eating as much, I have to enjoy every bite. You can't rush that. You could read some of our book while I finish?"

Bethany and I usually have a book to read aloud together in the car, so she pulled that out, but drifted away after a paragraph. The jetlag won't go down that easily.

For dessert I spread Patamilka [11] on a piece of toast.

"Now what is *that* supposed to be?" Bethany asked, unimpressed.

---

11 A heavenly French spin on Nutella

"Don't knock it till you try it, this right here is a French delicacy."

"That's as much of a French delicacy as *you* are."

I smiled proudly for a moment and then thought better.

"Hey! Take it back!"

"Yeah whatever. Let me a try a little."

We cleaned up and turned out the lights, looking forward to testing a €4 bottle of wine in our new and improved room. I don't need anyone to tell me I'll miss these days.

Monday, January 20, 2020 – Indy Galore

Reading, working out, cooking, cleaning, and practicing French before football practice. This is a "typical day" I could get used to. Bethany came to practice and did some pre medical school anatomy studying in the office while we were on the field. During individual periods, I kept looking over my shoulder, hoping that Paul would call us over for a team drill. It was all I could do to prepare forty-minutes worth of drills, but after an hour I called for another water break.

Moose and Sofian seemed relieved and rushed to their bottles. Meanwhile Brian and Aadil stayed put.

"We just had a water break, we're good. What's next?"

I wish I knew. I was flat out of drills. Thankfully Washnee, or, "big dick," as he preferred to be called, started calling out orders in French, and we fell in line for some of his drills. I joined Washnee, Aadil, and Mamadi, our athletic young tackle with serious raw talent, while James split off with Sofian, Moose, and Brian.

Washnee was talking to Mamadi and I worked on hand placement with Aadil. I'd put him at 5'8, 170 lbs., but he started at left tackle last season. I quickly learned that he was serious about the game, though, and was impressed by his attention to detail. He coached the youth team with Brian and seemed to be taking mental notes on everything I did, ready to pass on his new tricks.

I looked into the stands and saw Bethany sitting with a small group of ladies. *Yes, friends!* Afterwards at dinner, she told us they played on the women's football team.

"Wait hold on, you're saying the girls have a team here too? Like, tackle football?" James couldn't believe it. I couldn't either.

"Yeah apparently. They want me to come to practice with them sometime. We'll see about that. But their coach is a surgical nurse at the hospital next to us and said I could come shadow anytime!"

Tuesday, January 21, 2020 – Blindfold Pie

The tram was so crowded, it was difficult to find a spot to stand. I feel like a local when I brave the same hassles and pleasures as the good people of La Courneuve. Not a tourist, just another guy trying to fit onto the tram at rush hour. *Pardon, merci, pardon s'il vous plait.* I learn a little bit of French every day. When I pick up a new phrase, I'll use it with everyone I see.

Football players have a subtle idea that the coach ought to be able to practice everything he preaches. Even the oldest and most out of shape coaches could get the job done if only the rules would allow! But now the rules do allow, and it makes me feel like a hypocrite. During one-on-ones, Mamadi kept getting beat on inside moves. "À l'intérieur en premier, à l'extérieur en second. Très facile!" [12] I shouted at him.

---

12 *"Mamadi! Inside first, outside second! Very easy!"*

The very next play I stepped up for a rep at left tackle, overset [13] the defensive end, and got cooked on an inside move. I looked over at Mamadi.

"Très facile, oui?" He laughed.

My best coaching moment of the day came in instituting a long overdue snap count during one-on-ones. Offensive linemen are, admittedly, less athletic than the defense, and have to kick backwards while the defense barrels forward. With the deck stacked against us, the snap count becomes our best friend. It gives you the split second needed to level the playing field. Now, instead of going on "set hut" every rep, Moose stood behind the defense, showing us one, two, or three fingers while Aadil made the call at quarterback. *Set hut! Set hut... hut!* Five straight D linemen jumped offsides, to Michel's outrage. Once they had to react to *our* movement, we shut them down. Even Sofian held his own against a younger tackle, and we swarmed him in celebration!

During the customary speeches after practice, an epic steam rose from the group. We had just taken off our shoulder pads, and the heat from a hard practice met the frigid air. Europe may be more temperate than the U.S. due to ocean currents, but a January night this far North will be cold no matter where you are.

***

There's something virtuous about waking up early and getting your day going. Bethany chides me for attaching virtue to preferences, so maybe this is an instance of concept creep. [14] I thought at first that early

---

13 Kicked out wider than I needed to, giving up inside leverage and giving him space to beat me inside

14 Expanding concepts beyond their original boundaries, thereby bringing the implications of those concepts past where they originally ought to have been limited

mornings would come once the jet lag wore off, but here we are, hanging out in the kitchen at midnight. Consider this, though: if you work the late shift, you shouldn't get up early the next morning. You need your sleep. By the time we're home from practice, showered, and ready for dinner, it's past 11:00 PM. Then it becomes a matter of spending your waking hours during the beauty of the day or the magic of the night. It looks like we'll be choosing the night more often than not.

In the kitchen after practice, James told us about the show he'd been watching all day.

"Broo, this show is freakin *nuts*. So this dude runs a bookshop, right? But he gets *obsessed* with girls and ends up killing them. Tommy you'd like him though, cuz of the books. And he's really smart. But like, he's crazy about this girl so far, I dunno what he's about to do I'll probably finish it tonight though."

I was ready to kindly dismiss this nonsense when Bethany jumped in.

"Oh, *You*, right? That show is crazy!"

"Bro yes! *That's* what it's called!"

"You've seen this??" I looked at Bethany.

"Oh please, everyone's seen *You*." Turning to James, "Wait until you see what he does to her friends, I won't give away the ending though."

"Sounds... interesting. Alright let's get to our first challenge."

One of our wedding gifts was a scratch off book with adventurous challenges for couples. We'd stopped by Carrefour on the way back to get the ingredients, and now it was time to start... the blindfold pie. One person had to be totally blindfolded, and with nothing but voice instructions from the other, bake a pie. Easy enough, right? Well, yes, actually. Bethany was a pro, and only needed my help making sure she didn't burn herself on the toaster oven. Thirty minutes later, we sat down and victoriously shared the creation with our pals, to rave reviews.

"So tell me this," Sotiris asked, "I see memes of country music. What is this like? Can you play some songs?"

I'm no expert by American standards, but was happy to oblige. Country music has a unique place in the American spirit and I've grown to appreciate it. We devoured the pie to George Strait, Zach Brown, John Denver, and Toby Keith.

Wednesday, January 22, 2020 – Barcelona?

I finished the last spicy dumpling and leaned back, satisfied. After a quick and painless film session, Bruno ordered Chinese takeout. He and Mariannick were happy to hear that we were enjoying ourselves so far.

"So you plan to visit other places?" Mariannick asked.

"Yeah, we just aren't quite sure where or when. People always told us about how cheap the flights were in Europe, but I haven't found any of those yet. Same with the trains."

Bruno chimed in, "You want that I help you find good time to travel? We can look at calendar and search for good price."

We wanted to travel, but were having a terrible time finalizing anything. Bruno, it seemed, could help.

"Yeah that'd be great, thanks!"

"I show you the best sites to search for good prices, and we will look at the calendar to find good time for you to go." He fired up his computer. Bruno's office was well kept and covered in sports memorabilia. "Now where is it you want to go?"

"We were thinking Barcelona, Madrid, or Lisbon, depending on the prices." Bethany replied.

"Yes, yes those are very fine places. We will see the best prices. I use Skyscanner, it search Vueling, Ryanair, EasyJet... all of the low cost airlines." He flipped through a desk calendar. "This the last weekend of February may be good time for you to go. We have bye week, you can even leave Wednesday, just miss one practice Thursday, it's good."

"Are you sure that would be okay? Missing a practice?"

"Yes, yes that's okay, we want you to have a good time here. And like I say we have no game for two weeks here."

"Alright, should I run it by Paul first or do you think we can just book it?"

"You can if you like, but ultimately it is up to me and I say you can go, but you can tell him just to be in agreement yes."

Bruno had an itinerary in the shopping cart, ready to book a five day trip; two nights in Barcelona, two in Lisbon. We'd find a cheap Airbnb and get away for less than €300! Just then Paul walked by. I caught his attention and stepped outside to talk to him.

"Hey Paul, we were looking at a trip and Bruno found flights for a weekend in February. It would have us miss Thursday practice that week but Bruno said that was alright. Just wanted to check and make sure you were good with that?"

Paul's smile disappeared, replaced by an uncomfortable grimace.

"Ummm, that's *tough*."

I paused, confused and waiting for him to say more. He struggled to find the right words.

"That's tough."

"Okay, uh, so it wouldn't really be alright to miss that?"

"Well, you know, you are the only ones who are paid, and if the guys see you don't come to practice, they may get, well, uhm... that's tough."

Bruno noticed the tension and walked out. I stepped back into the office with Bethany while he and Paul exchanged some rapid French. Paul gave us an awkward smile, waved, and walked away. Bruno confidently strolled back into the office.

"Okay you are ready to purchase the flights?"

I was flustered. *Am I missing something? What just happened? Are they on the same page or not?* We had already sat here for an hour and I was desperate to get something on the calendar. Bruno was in charge, but Paul had the boots on the ground. He knew how this could impact the team dynamics. *Think, find a compromise. Make yourself and Bruno happy by booking something, and Paul happy by not missing practice.*

"Umm, could we actually see if there are flights another weekend in February? Leaving Friday and coming back Monday morning? We would be happy just going to Barcelona."

"Yes this is no problem, let me look." He clicked around for another minute. I knew I wasn't thinking straight, but saw the end in sight. "Yes here we have flight to Barcelona, Friday to Monday, good price. Last weekend in February, no game so you can go."

There it is, let's go. Close it and get out of here.

"Great! Yes let's book it. Basic economy."

Sitting next to me, Bethany sent me a text, "Maybe we should do this tomorrow after we look at the calendar to make sure this is the right call?"

"I think we're good let's just finish it if you're okay with that.'

"Yeah alright."

My tunnel vision narrowed while I read off our credit card information to Bruno. *We'd be spending three nights in a city restaurants are named after, that George Ezra wrote a song about. We could practice our Spanish and do it all on a budget!* It wasn't long after we'd placed the order that reason crept back into my brain and a terrible thought scattered the good feelings. *There was something on the calendar in February. Please don't be that weekend please don't be that weekend...* I opened up our Google Calendar for February 28 – March 1. *Blake and Mary visit.* Son of a sea serpent!!

Blake Hance, one of my groomsmen who had spent the past season on the Jaguars practice squad, and his girlfriend Mary, had booked flights and were planning on spending that exact weekend with us in Paris. For a moment, I thought of everyone else I could blame for this debacle, but quickly realized I was the only one. And then I wanted to slap myself! *Did your canny wife not suggest slowing things down and checking the calendar? What a pathetic husband! By the way, how could you get so flustered that you became irrational from some minor drama? What a loser!*

Stepping out of the office, Bethany was bothered but became more concerned when she saw I was livid with myself.

"Okay calm down, we can go to Barcelona another time. The most we can lose from this is €150, we'll be fine. As long as we don't, um, do this again." She gave me a smile telling me it was alright but probably just this one time.

Friday, January 24, 2020 – 1917

I was surprised by how familiar it felt. Like waking up from a dream, but noticing enough oddities to make you wonder if you were still asleep. Couples on dates, groups of friends, posters, popcorn, red couches. If I could just tune out the French voices and focus on the Post Malone song playing in the lobby, I might convince myself we were back in Century 12 Evanston. But no, this was UGC Ciné Cité Paris, and we were here to see a movie.

1917 had taken the entertainment world by storm, with its vivid World War I battle scenes and innovative cinematography. An achievement in filmmaking! I convinced Bethany to watch a series of Crash Course YouTube videos to refresh our memory on the nationalism, technology, and systems of alliances that created the "war to end all wars."

We splurged on some popcorn that reminded me just how epic American food portions are relative to Europe, and took a series of escalators up to our theatre on the fifth floor. Badis told us that Hollywood movies are all the rage, and that most Parisians prefer the English versions with French subtitles. Given the state of our French, that was just fine with us. Our showing of 1917 would be VOSTF, or, "version originale sous-titres français." [15]

We walked into the dark theatre and settled in for two hours of suspense. The terror was astonishing. One hundred years ago, artists like Hemingway from the lost generation had moved to Paris to make sense of the horrors they experienced in World War I; here we were today, removed by time but still grappling with the same questions.

Why were naïve young men sent to kill and be killed? What place does mercy have in war? Does heroism do anything but delay the inevitable? Was there meaning in the chaos?

---

15 *"Original language version, French subtitles"*

After the credits rolled, the projector pointed out a *Sortie* [16] at the bottom of the theatre. We were lost in thought discussing the movie until we stepped outside and the night demanded our attention. A fog had dropped. It was late, and this once charming urban neighborhood near La Périphérique felt eerily similar to the hostile streets we just walked with the endangered characters. Shadows passed under yellow streetlights and disappeared back into the mist. We geared up for the kilometer walk back to Line Seven. Leaving the theatre's welcoming lights, we passed shuttered shops and crossed an old bridge over *Canal de Saint-Denis*. Neither of us would be altogether surprised if an artillery shell passed overhead, or a bayonet laden Nazi started chasing us. A motorcycle with two men came from behind and passed us on the sidewalk, missing Bethany by a foot. It faded into the fog, slowed to a stop, and turned back towards us.

"Let's cross here, the train's on that side anyways." Bethany suggested.

"Oh sure, fine with me." The spookiness was losing its luster, but I wasn't ready to admit that.

No one else seemed to be innocently minding their own business that night. Two men stood in a streetlight across the intersection, silhouetted heads turning with us as we walked along. One hundred meters to the metro. A car slowed down as it passed by us. I stopped trying to talk about the movie. A hooded man with a facemask limped towards us out of the fog, made a close pass, and continued on. Just as I turned my head forward, he swung around and closed in behind us. I braced and stepped in front of Bethany, while he took a left and limped across the street. I looked back at Bethany with a nervous laugh, no he-man now.

She gave me a knowing look.

---

16   "Exit"

"Umm, I was just checking to.. uh.. let's get back and have some of that chocolate."

Saturday, January 25, 2020 – Idyllic Exploration

In today's mix: chopped jalapeños and red pepper along with gouda cheese, roasted potatoes, four eggs, olive oil, and Merguez sausage.

"Oh man! This is so good, we ought to give it a name."

"Tommy!" She's laughing, but exasperated. "You don't have to name everything!"

"When it's this good, it deserves a name!"

"Yeah alright, any brilliant ideas?"

"Why yes, if you're asking. This will forever be known as: *The Bobigny Scramble*. What do you think?"

"Not very creative, but yeah sure. It'll be fun to cook for visitors, showing hospitality, hosting and all. Who is for sure coming?"

"Well Blake and Mary will be the first ones, last weekend in February, you know the weekend we're not going to Barcelona?"

"How could I forget."

"And then my parents are coming towards the end of March. We were talking about hitting the *actual* Tulip Festival in the Netherlands while they're here."

"Not the knockoff in Holland, no disrespect to *Pure Michigan*."

"Yeah watch yourself. Anyways, James Prather[17] booked a flight for some time in May. We talked about trying to go to Moscow. We'll see about that."

On we talked, enjoying the Bobigny Scramble and plotting out our travels. Late January felt like Sophomore

---

17 A college teammate, groomsman, aspiring literature professor, and semi-professional dancer

year of high school. We had the lay of the land, but plenty of time to dream about the future. We'd just booked cheap Ryanair flights to Stockholm in April and were eying Prague for a free weekend in June. But today, we had our sights set on something closer to home. One of the consistent recommendations I heard before leaving was to see Montmartre. [18]

A quaint artisan neighborhood overlooking Paris from the Eighteenth, [19] Montmartre famously houses *Basilique du Sacré-Cœur*. [20] France built this stunning church as a means of restoring national pride in the wake of defeat in the Franco-Prussian war. Construction started in 1875, and Sacré-Cœur was dedicated in 1919. Today, it's the second most visited landmark in the city.

Only time will tell if The Bobigny Scramble etches its way into the French imagination, but this batch was gone and we were ready to go. Starting to get the hang of things, we took Line Seven to *Stalingrad*, switched to Line Two and continued on to *Avers*. Stepping out of the metro station can be disorienting, but knowing Sacré-Cœur stood at the highest point in the city, we headed uphill. Along the way, the crowds thickened and tourist knick-knack shops replaced local necessities in the storefronts.

While I will join the chorus in chiding gimmicky souvenirs, they are fun to look at. What colors, symbols, landmarks, and ideas make up the *itness* of a place? That's exactly what tourist shops ask and then distill into small affordable products. Pirate keychains and palm tree bottle

---

18 WARNING: do not attempt to pronounce this word in public until you have taken two years of college level French. It will be as embarrassing as it is futile. But for what it's worth, "Mone-marrrr...(t)" will get you close

19 One of twenty arrondissements, or, administrative districts, in Paris

20 "Sacred Heart Basilica"

openers in Tampa. Desk sized Mayan ruins in Cozumel. Pine candles and moose ornaments in the North Woods. A knock off Constitution in D.C. In these Parisian shops, we saw the Eifel Tower, Arc de Triomphe, Sacré-Cœur, Le Chat Noir, the Louvre's pyramid, Notre Dame, Moulin Rouge, impressionist paintings, baguettes, croissants, lavender, berets, snails, and scarves. The French flag was printed on T-shirts, plates, hats, magnets, towels, and anything else you can think of smaller than a microwave. Under no illusions that I'd be mistaken for a fashionable Frenchman, I picked up a €3 scarf, looping it around my neck like I'd seen my teammates do after practice.

We made it out of these shops with minimal damage and continued uphill to the main attraction. The church was spectacular, matched only by the breathtaking view of the city below us. The white domes looked like the Taj Mahal. Groups of tourists swarmed the promenade, jockeying for position to snap a picture. Others sat on benches or stairs, taking it in. The inside was even more impressive. All of the interior artwork was mosaic. Thousands of small tiles created everything from paper-sized portraits to an enormous profile of Jesus with a golden heart, covering the entire apse. [21]

We finished our lap and walked down to the crypt, which was retrofitted with lights and projectors. Displays told the story of the Bible and Jesus' life. In an increasingly secular Europe, touring cathedrals may be one of the only touchpoints many people have with the church, and I'm glad to see Sacré-Cœur shares their true purpose with visitors.

We walked out of the crypt to a beautiful panorama. The winter sun had nearly set, leaving a pink glow hanging above the hazy city, just as the twinkling lights were coming to life. Every hour on the hour, between 6:00 PM

---

21 The inside of a half-circle dome in a church, usually above the alter

and midnight, the Eifel Tower sparkles from head to toe. Standing atop the tower, the strobe lights are blinding, but from across the city, it was a smooth glimmer bringing life to the dusk. The spotlight beam swept over us and continued on its beat.

The streets we walked from there were exactly what I've always pictured Paris to be like. Winding narrow stone streets between up-lit classic buildings, with cafés and bistros on the street level and apartments above. We stumbled upon *Place du Tertre*, a square filled with artists under the watchful eye of patrons eating, drinking, and smoking at tables outside of cafés. We paid €3 for a bag of freshly roasted chestnuts and strolled by the easels. It wasn't far and there was no rush, so we walked to see Moulin Rouge, the famous cabaret theatre. With prices starting around €185, we had no interest in a show, but did enjoy the mesmerizing windmill on the roof.

Once home, we opened our Adventure Challenge book and scratched one off. *Go back to the good old days. Build a blanket fort and watch a movie together.* Consider it done. Bethany poured two glasses of Martinelli *Minervois wine* while I rigged up a suitable structure. Thankfully, this was my specialty back in the day, and I had our comforter secured over the desk chairs in no time. We sat back, raised a toast to the good life, and fell asleep to a tale from the French countryside. [22]

Sunday, January 26, 2020 – EIC

"We describe ourselves as a community of sojourners, empowering one another to cultivate Gospel transformation." I'd heard this a hundred times, every

---

22 *Chocolat*, if you're wondering. A nice movie starring a young Johnny Depp and critiquing sanctimonious churchgoers. One takeaway – omission and commission both matter! Matthew 23:23

Sunday morning during the announcements at Evanston Bible Fellowship, my church home throughout college. One word was especially poignant. *Sojourners.* We're all passing through this world, but in a college town, most people were especially transient. The point was, *be invested while you're here.* I thought of that while we rode the RER [23] down to Emmanuel International Church. We only had half of the year, but wanted to be connected during that time.

Finding a church wasn't as hard as I feared. Narrow your search to English speaking and Bible believing, and there was one that jumped out. EIC was an hourlong trip from Stade de Mode, but as long as we could read, look around, or think, the time never felt like a waste. We arrived a few minutes early and were greeted by a kind looking American with glasses who welcomed us and had to run. We found a seat and watched the rest of the congregation trickle in. It appeared to be mostly American expats, though I heard a few French accents mixed in. We sang songs extolling the greatness of God and thanking him for his mercy. The man who greeted us, KJ, preached a sermon, walking us through a passage in First Peter. Everyone was invited to walk to a nearby mall afterwards for a time of fellowship.

Bethany and I picked up a snack from Marks and Spencer [24] and got to know our new church family. A Marine Corps officer and his family, stationed in the embassy. A supply chain manager for GE, fresh off of an assignment in Singapore. An au pair, taking care of two young kids during her gap year before college. A British mathematician, now lecturing at the Sorbonne. A Spanish businesswoman whose English was better than

23 The regional commuter train system. This train is faster and makes fewer stops, with the intention of connecting the suburbs to the city center

24 A London-based retailer

her French. A struggling jazz musician. They were from all walks of life and warmly welcomed us.

"You really mean American football? Like with touchdowns and everything?"

"I guess we'll have to bring a group to a game sometime!"

"I had no idea they played that here!"

"We're glad you two came!"

We left thankful to have found a church community, albeit for a short time. It's always better to be an invested sojourner!

***

Back in Stade de Mode's kitchen, we sat with Badis, Sotiris, and James having dinner and catching up. I told them about our trip to EIC and connecting with the expats.

"Oh I'm so happy for this! You come to Paris and you can find your church and countrymen." Badis seemed genuinely pleased.

We kept talking until Sotiris, who had been looking down at his phone, gasped and showed his screen to Badis, who was similarly shocked. They talked back and forth in hurried French, Badis demanding verification of whatever Sotiris had shown him. He kept scrolling until Badis looked sadly convinced.

"We just find out Kobe Bryant has died!"

"Yes there was helicopter crash, his daughter dies too. So sad."

I couldn't believe this, and a quick look at the Flash WhatsApp group told me my teammates couldn't either. Kobe seemed invincible, barely human. He had everything; he was a legend. This wasn't supposed to happen!

It left me in a somber mood as I prepared for the next week. I loved the season's cadence, but the long weekends could get my mind out of football mode. In America, once the season started, there was never any question about it. I was on a campaign. Now, I found myself flipping back and forth between work and play. But our first game was coming this week. Time to lock in!

Bethany in the Hall of Mirrors, Versailles.

Paris was much better with Bethany.

CHAPTER III

Spartiates

Monday, January 27, 2020 - Cheers

At Fitness Park this morning, I recognized a younger face from the Flash with long curly hair, working out across the room. I went over to say hello.

"Ça va, mon ami?" [1]

"Toommy! Yes yes good, very good! And you? You are good too yes?"

His English was broken, but certainly better than my French.

"Yeah doing well, I'm sorry I forgot your name."

"It is good! I am Yassine!"

"Yassine! Thanks, how long have you been with the Flash?"

"This is my first year with Elite team, I play with Flash when I was young. I hope I go United States to play JUCO, earn scholarship. Look and see this now."

He pulled out his phone and proceeded to show me some of his highlights on Instagram. Chasing down

---

1 *"Are you alright, my friend?"*

a running back for a backfield tackle, catching a pass for a ten-yard gain. He was very proud.

"That's pretty good, you wanna lift with me today?"

"Yes this is good! We work together now!"

He was a great lifting partner, eager to help put the weights away and trying to imitate my form on the exercises. I couldn't shake the feeling that he'd never get the chance to chase a dream that millions of American boys take for granted. Yassine was nineteen, spoke broken English, and likely didn't have much money. He was athletic, but not elite. A truly exceptional athlete can find an opportunity from almost anywhere, but what about someone like him? He could have been a great high school football player. Maybe he'd go on to play Division III or NAIA, get an education, and move into a career proud of his time as a football player. For most football players in La Courneuve, playing for the Flash elite team throughout their twenties would be enough; it would be a dream come true. But for the ones who wouldn't be satisfied unless they made it to America, would they ever be content?

***

Today was the first game planning practice. In college, Mondays were a mental day, spent mostly in the meeting room. We'd install the game plan, learn about the opponent's defense, and run through plays without pads. Usually we'd lift weights afterwards. Coaches expected everyone to watch hours of film on their iPad at home.

James and I arrived at the office around 6:00 PM to watch film with Paul. The practice plan predicted an offensive meeting at 7:30. Paul waited hopefully in the office for a quorum that never came, and around 8:00 we walked down to the locker room. Eventually we had a critical mass and Paul started drawing on the whiteboard.

For about an hour, he went over coverages, defensive fronts, tendencies, and plays we'd run. Rico, a trilingual German tight end, sat between James and me, translating. "He says expect the T-E stunt in cover two. Now he is talking to the wide receivers about their routes. He says to the offensive line, stick to our rules and sort out the blitzes. Now he says to Mamadi to pay attention, what is your assignment on the backside of outside zone? He is not happy with Mamadi."

We had our quarterback struggling to find a good marker in an unheated locker room with half of the offense, but it still felt familiar. I could have been in a two-hundred million dollar facility, listening to Coach Cushing prepare us for Ohio State. This was football.

Around 9:00 we made our way to the field, in helmets and shoulder pads, to run through plays until the lights went out. In the mad scramble after the pre-practice breakdown, we noticed a new face looking lost.

"Does anyone speak English??" He called in a crisp British accent.

Thankfully he was just meters away from two Americans who were very happy to speak some English. I felt like Doc Holliday in *Tombstone: "I'm your huckleberry!"*

"Yeah right here, what's up?"

"Americans! Thank God. Do you know where the defense is supposed to go?"

"Yeah right over there with coach Niko and the guys in black jerseys."

"Cheers, I'll see you around."

Such a simple interaction, but I loved it. Marco was from London, where he played college football. He recently moved to Paris for a job and came to check out the local football team. Connections form quickly with a commonality in a world of differences. I also felt a bit of Anglo-American pride, considering our shared histories and modern allyship. Two cultures, forever intertwined! I could see Bethany rolling her eyes.

After practice, Niko repeatedly hit on a topic I've never had to worry about.

"You all must pay the league dues before you can play on Saturday. If you do not pay league dues, you will not play." Marcus, a British educated linebacker, translated. I would have assumed he was a native speaker if I didn't know any better.

Not only was the rest of the team unpaid, they had to pay for their equipment and league dues. I thought Niko had moved on to something else, but Marcus continued,

"No one is special, everyone will pay. Talk to Bruno about a plan if you need to, but do not think you will be able to come Saturday if you do not pay, it will not be free. We do not have lots of money."

In college, resources were never an issue. In the NFL, money was part of the spectacle. Hyperbaric chamber? Check. New research thinks we might benefit from a cryotherapy chamber? Consider it done. Charter 737s? Just part of the business. Staff of chefs preparing made to order quesadillas? What would you like on it? Before tax weekly game checks for active roster players started around $40,000, but the league's highest paid players can make almost one hundred times that per week. [2]

Veteran players saw money as a renewable resource. *Hundred bucks I throw this bottle in the trash can? Bet!* One player told me the other linemen at the pro bowl gave him $3,000 to play right tackle for most of the game when they all wanted to play left.

Once during a meeting with the Falcons, the offensive line coach, Chris Morgan, asked me a strange question.

---

2   In 2020, the NFL's highest paid player is quarterback Patrick Mahomes, of the Kansas City Chiefs. He's slated to make $45,000,000 this year, not including any endorsements.

"Tommy would you do pretty much anything for $25,000? Like if I said we would give you the money in *this room*, you would probably do it no matter what?"

"Yeah I guess I probably would. What kind of thing are we talking about?"

He smirked at the veterans in the back row.

"Mt. Gushmore." My first thought was running up a hill until vomiting. Easy money. "We have a longstanding offer in the Falcons O-line room that if a rookie gets a tattoo covering his entire back with Mount Rushmore, but with the five starters as the faces, they'll each give him $5,000."

I do not currently have a giant back tattoo, nor an extra $25,000, but the scenario fascinated me. It was like one of those hypothetical games people love to play, but the money was actually on the table. $25,000 would be fantastic for someone making about one thousand per week in training camp, but it wasn't a life changing amount. Suppose they had said they'd each give $25,000. What then?? Do I take the offer? Invest that money and watch it grow? Pay for tattoo removal surgery? I don't think anyone on the Flash will give me the chance to make a decision on that one.

Back in Stade de Mode, I microwaved a box of noodles, expecting it to taste like any American expects a microwavable noodle box to taste like. Instead, it was delicious. Buttery noodles with meaty red sauce, unreasonably fresh and tasty. I checked the side of the box and it listed only five ingredients. I was indignant. Why can't we have nice things like this in America??

I sat down with my gourmet noodle box for the nightly ritual of unwinding in the kitchen with Badis, James, Bethany, and occasionally Sotiris or one of the track and field runners. Badis' knowledge of American culture continues to amaze me. We tried showing him four Key and Peele videos before finding one he hadn't already seen. We listened to songs from each other's pre game playlists, and talked about our favorite movies.

"Broo, you seen that movie *Sing*, with the animals doing a singing competition?"

"Oh yeah with Matthew McConaughey? I love that one!"

"Yeah bro I've literally watched that one like two hundred times. *Conservative* estimate."

"Two *hundred* times?? No you didn't! That's like weeks of watching it."

"I swear it's true man! That was like the only thing me and my ex could agree on."

Tuesday, January 28, 2020 – Cooperation

We woke up earlier today so that Bethany could make it to *Hopital Avicienne* by 8:30. I made her some coffee and a humble breakfast while she got ready for a day of shadowing. Renaud, the surgical nurse who coaches the women's team, had set her up to scrub in and observe a day of orthopedic operations. We took the short walk to the hospital together. It felt like a compound, with multiple perimeters and security checkpoints.

"Have fun saving some lives today!" I kissed her goodbye.

"If I end up touching any patients, something has gone seriously wrong!" She called over her shoulder.

I laughed and watched her walk into the surgery wing, like a proud parent nervously sending my child off to school.

I spent most of the day before practice reading and catching up on the news. An impeachment trial in the senate, a virus outbreak in China. None of it seemed to matter as much as it used to. I read Wikipedia articles about medium sized cities in Central Asia, wondering what life would be like there. I'd pause to worry about Bethany, who I had no way of communicating with, then I'd relax thinking about God's sovereignty and her four minute walk home. I read a few chapters from *Soccer Empire*.

Soccer Empire traces the history of France's imperial empire, and follows that history to the current debates over multiculturalism. Should immigrants assimilate with the majority culture? Or expand upon and add to it? How should modern France interact with its former colonies? France's national soccer team offers a window into this societal drama. The team looks like France's colonial empire. Most of the players are Black and Arab and have lived the struggles of colonialism and immigration.

The book answers random questions that have popped up walking the streets. A burnt car sitting on the side of the road, to no one's surprise but mine? Driving is expensive in France, and cars are a sign of status and privilege, making their incineration a popular form of protest. [3]

I ended my erudite afternoon memorizing the lyrics to *Les Champs-Elysees*, a classic French ditty about the famous avenue. While I may be able to entertain my teammates by knowing the chorus of one French song, I have to live with the consequences of an earworm for at least the rest of the day. Listening to the band in my head on the tram to practice, I wasn't holding on for a sudden stop that sent me flailing across the car, landing safely in an older woman's lap. She sent me away with some French that I can only assume meant, *"I'm glad you're okay, but don't let it happen again you oversized yardbird."*

My tram mishaps didn't stop there. Some people are dead-set on avoiding any sort of interaction. But when a tram gets crowded, you are past the point of not

3 "Burn." Soccer Empire: the World Cup and the Future of France, by Laurent Dubois, University of California Press, 2011, pp. 214-215.

needing to cooperate. We need to work together a little! One younger man only moved slightly when I tried to pass him and get off in front of Stade Geo Andre, hoping that by avoiding eye contact, we'd pass like two ships in the night. There simply was not enough space for that. I can't move through obstacles like a cat, and while I tried my best to get skinny and pass him, once we got to my midsection, I was pressed against him with enough force that my continuing to move brought him along, like I had attached a large Velcro strip. He was horrified as the wave that was me swept him through the tram before I had space to decouple. To his immense credit, however, he returned to his spot without ever making eye contact.

***

We spent most of practice running carded plays against the defense. On a fully stocked football team, a squad, usually of younger or second string players, spends the week running the opponent's offense or defense against the starters. The scout team. Without the numbers to do this, our starters took turns running the Spartiates plays against the other side of the ball. As the scout team, we did our best to read a new play on the card and execute against our stalwart defensive line, to mixed results. Niko hounded us, never satisfied with our efforts.

One of the marks of a mature offensive lineman in the U.S. is the ability to understand where you have help and where the defender has to play, and use that to your advantage. Otherwise, it's very difficult to play fast. *If the linebacker is out of the box in an even front with a slide in my direction, I can set more aggressively to his outside shoulder, since the guard is watching my inside.* I got better at this over the years, but none of that seems to matter now. Linebackers and defensive linemen run wherever they please. I've been beat a few times when I assumed someone would go where I wanted them to.

We went through the usual post practice speeches and locker room handshakes, and I sauntered to the tram. I was sore. I feel the aches and pains of practice, but also fifteen previous years of football. I still believe there's enough in my tank to give my best this season, but retirement stalks me. Limping towards the tram under a streetlight, I can feel it breathing down my neck. Fingers, hands, ankles, elbows, back, hips, feet, neck. There's some kind of pain everywhere. I feel old and tired of the contact. It amazes me that I have teammates pushing through this well into their adult lives. The American pipeline ends once you're no longer good enough. In France, it's indefinite.

January 29, 2020 – Chew Some Gum

Yassine joined me for an upper body lift at Fitness Park. At his age, I was under the watchful eye of professional coaches, surrounded by teammates, training in a state of the art facility dedicated to football. He was waiting for a middle aged woman to finish using a bench so that he could continue a lift I made up on the walk over.

Resources matter in weight training. At Northwestern, after a lift I would down two protein shakes, a bottle of cherry juice, and Gatorade before heading up to a nutritious all you can eat buffet. In the NFL, it was more of that plus ligament strengthening gelatin, amino acid chain mixes, creatine, and a probiotic drink. Here, after the lift I walked fifteen minutes to get home before drinking a cup of water and chewing some gum.

With another free evening, we looked at the map and picked a new neighborhood to explore. Today it would be the Latin Quarter. Sitting on the left bank in the Fifth, this neighborhood once hosted Hemingway and other writers of The Lost Generation. The namesake comes from Latin, once the lingua-franca of the many universities scattered about the area. I spotted students studying in the Sorbonne's library and felt nostalgic for my time in Evanston.

We strolled past the Pantheon, Luxembourg Gardens, and the Shakespeare and Company Bookstore. None of them were open, but were pretty enough from the outside. We walked north and crossed the river into the First, towards the opera building and a spot Bruno insisted we check out. Legend has it that Tod Sloan opened a bar in New York in the early twentieth-century. To his dismay, alcohol was outlawed in 1920. Not to be deterred, he dismantled the bar piece by piece, and shipped it to Paris, opening Harry's New York Bar.

The interior retains its prohibition era charm, and the walls are covered in college pennant flags. I found Northwestern's prominently displayed near the front door – go cats. The only letdown was the price column on the drink menu. We might as well have been in Yankee Stadium. We took our time, making darn sure to enjoy my €9 beer and Bethany's €15 cocktail, a raspberry and elderflower gin drink called The Angie.

Since we were in the neighborhood, I insisted we walk past the American embassy, next to *Place de la Concorde*.[4] Bethany graciously listened to my embassy monologue.

"Just think of it! A little piece of America, right here in Paris! But not just here, hundreds of embassies and consulates throughout the world! Beacons of freedom

---

4 A grand roundabout centered on a 75 foot tall obelisk from the Luxor Temple, which ended up in Paris after an 1833 trade with Ottoman Egypt. The other side of the trade, a mechanical clock, was damaged in transport and never worked. You can still see it today in Cairo, just bring a watch.

and cooperation, but symbols of the West, and therefore targets! So they hold security and beauty in a delicate balance! Benjamin Franklin, Thomas Jefferson, and James Monroe all occupied this post..."

"Yes that's interesting." Bethany wasn't just humoring me. She genuinely takes interest in the things that fascinate me and gives me space to wonder about them. It's a gift, and I try to reciprocate. We're both richer for opening ourselves to the other's passions.

As I'm sure Jefferson and Franklin did when they couldn't afford dinner at Harry's New York Bar, we stopped by Burger King for dinner, a bold protest of the exorbitant prices. I regret to report that Burger King is absolutely no better in France.

Thursday, January 30, 2020 – Coup de Boul

If sports are a microcosm of greater societal struggles, the case in point may be Zinedine Zidane's famous headbutt, or as the French say, *coup de boul.*[5] In the final minutes of the 2006 World Cup Final versus Italy, what would be the last game of Zidane's storied career, "Zizou," as the fans knew him, turned and delivered a headbutt to Marco Materazzi's chest. It was as devastating to Materazzi as it was shocking to the world. One of the greatest players of all time left the field for the last time, in disgrace. Italy won in a penalty kick shootout.

Today, however, memories vary depending on whom you ask. An Italian will mock Zidane and boast in their victory. An outside observer may vaguely remember

5   "Coup de Boul." *Soccer Empire: the World Cup and the Future of France*, by Laurent Dubois, University of California Press, 2011, pp. 241-266

seeing it on TV. But ask a French man living in a *banlieu*,[6] and you get a different answer.

"Hey Washnee," I asked in the locker room before practice, "what do you think of Zidane, the coup de boul?"

"Zidane?! Zidane is president of France! He is god!" He turned to a group beside us and spit out a stream of excited French. I caught something about the *coup de boul* and Materazzi.

The group erupted in a chorus of curses to Materazzi's name.

"F****** Materazzi!"

"All of France hate him!"

"He is son of b****!"

"So did Zidane do a good thing? The coup de boul?" I asked, surprised by the visceral reaction. The group looked over to Washnee.

"Oh course he does! Zidane, he stands up for his self! He has right to not be.. I don't know how to say.. provoke! Yes! He does right thing."

Now this is interesting. Was it more than just national pride? Zidane, the son of Algerian immigrants, grew up in Saint-Denis. Perhaps my teammates found in his headbutt a sense of agency, where someone like them had the right to stand up against provocations? An affirmation that they deserved more respect than they had received? On paper, this seems simple. Materazzi was wrong for whatever he said, Zidane was wrong for his reaction. But somehow it feels more complicated.

During practice, our final before the first game, we started out with three offensive linemen. While we waited for more to show up, I talked to a Division II player who wandered over to talk with Moose. He was a forensic police officer. This caught my attention. I was just reading about civilian-police conflict in the banlieus;

---

6 Working class neighborhoods largely composed of immigrant families

many of the officers stationed in these neighborhoods are young men from rural towns who would rather not be there.[7] I asked him how he liked his work.

"I am sorry, I have little English. But, it is not good. I want to find new work. Very tough."

"Really? In what ways?"

"There is politics. We, uh, must meet numbers, and I see very bad things at Charlie Hebdo, you know this? And two thousand and fifteen terror attack. Very bad. I must do something else."

By the time team periods started, we had Moose, Sofian, Aadil, James, and me. The five of us must have run fifty plays, between offensive periods and scout team. It would be nice to forgo some lower pads[8] on Thursdays, but practice was just as physical as Tuesday, so I'll keep them on for now. In any good American practice, there's a premium on body control and staying off the ground. People get hurt when bodies fly around, and there's enough of that on gameday to keep the athletic trainers busy. Here, that's not much of a concern. Linebackers dive across the line of scrimmage, safeties go for knockout blows on the receivers, running backs lower their shoulder and hit the truck stick.

At Northwestern, the offense joked that Coach Fitz favored the defense. A, *Fitz loves the D!* chant occasionally rose from the sideline during practice after a holding call or tongue lashing to the running backs. His criticism was likely warranted more than we offensive players would care to admit, and we had one of the country's best defenses. On top of that, Fitz was twice named the

---

7 "Burn." *Soccer Empire: the World Cup and the Future of France*, by *Laurent Dubois*, University of California Press, 2011, pp. 232-233.

8 Offensive linemen, more than any other position, are weighed down with protective equipment. Ankle braces, knee braces, knee pads, a girdle with hip and thigh pads. We wouldn't trade the additional protection for anything, but when the coast is clear, it feels great to shed some of it.

nation's best defensive player while leading the cats in the nineties. It was an overwrought accusation, but a fun provocation nonetheless.

Niko was cut from the same defensive cloth. He had plenty to say to the offense after practice.

"The offense must be better, especially the scout team! Not enough plays! Not good enough! It will be your fault if the defense struggles on Saturday!" Marcus smirked and eventually stopped translating. "I think you get the point." He said with a wink.

Niko loves the D!

Friday, January 31, 2020 – The Night Before

Bethany and I spent the afternoon in the nearest establishment with reliable WI-FI, McDonalds. There will be plenty of opportunities for charming Parisian cafés, but today we just needed to use the internet. We planned a schedule for my family's visit in April. *Monday they can rest during the day, then we'll have a nice dinner and see the Eifel Tower at night. Tuesday and Wednesday we'll be around Paris, Thursday is Normandy, then we'll spend the weekend in the Netherlands!* We also made plans for Stockholm. A fjord boat tour, Viking museum, and traditional evening coffee looked nice.

Eventually we had to pack up and get home; I had plans tonight, even if I didn't know what they were. Doukie told us there was a tradition the night before the first game. Washnee was nearby and said he'd pick James and me up at 7:30 PM. He rolled up to Stade de Mode around 8:00, which I'm gathering is par for the course when it comes to French punctuality. James and I crammed into the backseat, behind Washnee and Nyor, who was sleeping in the passenger seat. Nyor was a massive lineman who hadn't been around much, but apparently would start at right guard tomorrow.

"Yo thanks for scoopin us, that's mad cool a' you." James chittered while he buckled in.

Washnee snapped his head up confused, eying me in the rearview mirror for help.

"Uhh, merci beacoup, por, umm, conduire."[9] I tried my best to translate.

I nailed my introduction with Washnee, and now he gives my French far too much credit, speaking rapidly or asking me to translate. When James asked where they lived, I got another mirror look from Washnee. Thankfully a recent DuoLingo lesson left me with just enough to get the job done.

"Ou est ton maison? C'est pres du Stade Geo Andre à La Courneuve?"[10] I somehow pieced together. This moment alone vindicated the hours I'd spent on that forsaken app.

"Ah yes! Yes close by, not far no not far."

James nodded, accepting it. Then he looked towards Nyor, sound asleep. "So he's pretty tired, huh?"

"Yes, very tired. He work all day, no sleep last night. Me too, I sleep three hour."

"What?? Were you guys working?" I couldn't believe it.

"Yes yes, we make extra money at night, work as, uh, at club! Security! We both work tonight too, then go home to sleep to game."

I can't say I've ever had to worry about two starting offensive lineman bouncing clubs the night before the game to complement their day jobs. I'd be embarrassed if he asked what I've been doing the last two days.

---

9   *"Thank you very much, for, drive."*

10   *"Where is your house? Is it near Stade Geo Andre in La Courneuve?"*

We drove southeast, passing through several banlieus outside of La Périphérique. I still had no idea what we were doing tonight, or how late we might be out. We came up to some commotion. Red flares lit up the nearby buildings. A crowd chanted together. James and I looked at each other in alarm, while Nyor slept and Washnee begrudgingly found a way around.

We finally parked on a street, not far from the demonstration, and walked a block before turning down a dark alley and into a loading dock area. It was dark and looked neglected. *Where were we?* I was holding a microwave and James had a massive bag that smelled like food, both from Washnee's trunk. Washnee pounded on the door to a building next to the loading dock and Dookie stepped out, welcoming us in. We walked into a room with a small stage in front of a few rows of folding tables and chairs, complete with a spotlight and flashing disco ball. The room was already packed with teammates who welcomed us the same way they did in the locker room.

Everyone seemed pleased to see us, especially the gifts we bore. There was a rush for our table when we set down the microwave and bag. Washnee started pulling out plastic containers full of rice and meat.

"This is food of Mali, very good! You will like it very much! You have spicy food yes?"

"Yeah I love spicy food!"

"We see how much you like spicy food after this! *Very* spicy!"

He wasn't kidding about the spice, but it was delicious. I found a table with the offensive line and made small talk while wolfing down a second container.

Doukie took the stage and the program began. Marcus, emerging as the best translator on the team, sat near us and relayed the instructions.

"Everyone on the team will go to the stage. You should say your name, how long you've been playing, tell about your family, work, personal goals, and team goals. And everyone must say something in English at the end, for you guys."

With a packed room of long winded speakers and an open microphone, you may not be surprised to hear this went on for hours. But I didn't care, I was enamored. Each player opened a window into his life and motivations.

The guys were honest. They didn't lie if they felt unmotivated or doubted their abilities. It was refreshing. Typically with football-types, you have to wonder what they really think and feel. I'm guilty of this myself. In the name of positivity, I spit out the *right* talking points, spinning my doubts and failures back towards the straight and narrow. My new teammates didn't seem to care.

Sofian (So), the inquisitive linebacker I met after the scrimmage, went first. "When I see someone on the field I learn about who they are in life too. We pay to play and what sets the Flash apart is our work ethic. Football is life."

Washnee implored us to play with violence and passion. Marcus laughed and facepalmed before finishing his translation. "He says he works tonight at a gay nightclub, and he won't tell if he sees anyone there."

In his obligatory English at the end, he addressed James and me, "And James, Tommy, welcome both to France. James I hope you will come to smoke with me sometime, and Tommy, I hope you have fun praying to Jesus!" He raised his hands in the air and started humming *Battle Hymn of the Republic*. Those who knew it joined in the song.

Amir was back with the Flash after spending last season playing for a rival team. "I just want to say I am happy to be back. I am sorry for the way I disrespected the Flash last year." I made a note to ask someone what happened.

Ryan also was returning to the Flash; he spent the past year in New Mexico. He took his time talking, wearing sweats and a beanie pulled down to his eyebrows. He squinted in the spotlight.

"I will be honest with you all, I am having a tough time. I went to America, it was my dream. I got to JUCO, and knew I could go to Division I, but my JUCO was a small military school in the desert. The coach didn't want us to leave. He was crazy man, swears he saw aliens. So he didn't play me and I didn't get recruited. And I got hurt too. I didn't love to play the game anymore. So I knew I had to come back to the Flash." He paused for a moment and looked down.

"This is my home, you guys are my family." And then he turned to us, saying in English, "Welcome to France Tommy and James. Stay Americans, don't become French when you play football. Work hard and give the standard you know you can, that's why you are here."

Something struck me about Ryan. We had wildly different backgrounds, yet at twenty-four, we were in the same place. Coming to La Courneuve, looking to fall in love with the game again after getting burned out in America.

Doukie wanted to spread American football, to show Europe that it was a great sport. "Be proud of what we are doing, we help the spread and growth of football."

Yuri reminded the Flash what makes the team special. "We work hard and give our best on the field, this is why we succeed. We are from many places but play as a family and stick together. Some people in France fear us when they see us, because of how we look, but on the football field that is a good thing. Then they see our passion and our skill and know who we really are."

It was Marcus' turn to talk, so Ryan, who sat next to us after talking, took over translating duties. Marcus had a thin mustache and a scar around his eye. He looked comfortable up front. "I work as artistic director for an advertisement agency. I want to be good at my job and be good at football. But I'll tell you, I am getting older, and don't think I'm that good. For the team's sake, I hope one of you young guys takes my starting spot."

In an effortless turn to English he looked towards us. "Tommy and James, when Paul talked to you, did he tell you that you'd be living in Paris? Or in La Courneuve?" About half the team understood it and laughed.

Charles, a smart defensive end, delivered an encouraging speech before turning to me and in broken but sly English said, "Tommy, I am glad that your wife she comes too. I hope that you will leave France maybe with a little one." We'll see about that!

Max, one of five or so white guys on the team, was a computer programmer who always seemed to be smiling. "When I came to the Flash, I thought I was going to play in the ghetto but instead I just found a family. Thank you guys. I will always give my best for you."

Axwell was a defensive end with legitimate Big Ten talent. If he were younger, I'd tell Northwestern to take a look at him. "Football has helped me. I want to mentor the young people living in banlieus. We can do many good things together." He turned to us and said sincerely, "welcome home."

Niko had been sitting in the back, and now walked towards the stage. When I saw him sitting on the stool, looking out at the team, I felt bad for the critical thoughts I often had during his long speeches after practice. He cared about the team and these players, and without a doubt knew how to win.

"My job is to make you better. I know you will not always like me, but I want you to get better. We all know 2019 was not a good year. We have pride and want to be better. Tomorrow is our first chance to show the Flash have returned. To Tommy and James, welcome. You remember that only you get paid, so we expect a lot from you. But no pressure, it is not good to be stressed. Have a good time here."

At the end, James and I had a chance to talk. James shared about himself, thanked the team, and predicted a championship. Marcus came up with us. For a minute I wanted to wing it in French, but realized I needed to say more than a second grade lexicon would allow.

"Bon soir mon amis, je suis Tommy and je suis de Michigan en les Etats-Unis. L'habit ici avec ma femme, Bethany, de ses moises. Je juis football American de quinze ans." That was all I could manage for now. "Marcus, un translation sil vous plait." [11]

Sitting on the stool I raised my hand to cover the spotlight and looked down at the sixty faces looking back at me. If I ever thought of giving less than my best, of coasting to the end of my football career, that would be unthinkable after tonight. These guys gave up sleep and time with their families to commit to the Flash. They had welcomed me with open arms, and given me an incredible gift - the opportunity to finish my career as part of a family again. To walk away from the game with my head held high and a good taste in my mouth. A chance to add something more to the team than an expendable body during training camp. Redemption.

"I want to thank you for welcoming me to the Flash. I was cut four times pursuing the NFL and was disappointed, because I wasn't good enough anymore, and football felt like a business where we did it for the money. I came to France to learn and to play for a brotherhood

---

11   "*Good evening my friends, I am Tommy and I am from Michigan in the United States. I live here with my wife, Bethany, of seven months. I play American football for fifteen years. Marcus, a translation please.*"

again. My personal goal is to give my very best to help the team, to see France, and build relationships, and my team goal is to win the championship after preparing well every time we train. Also, the sweat on my face is not because I'm nervous, but because the food of Mali is delicious and very spicy." That was only partially true, I was nervous. Enough people seemed to understand this to laugh before the translation came out.

Saturday, February 1, 2020 – Spartiates

Instead of coming down from the hotel room, leaving my garment bag by the door for a police dog to sniff, and walking into a stern dining hall for the pregame meal, I put some instant noodles in the microwave for a lighthearted lunch with Bethany, Badis, and James. Instead of pulling up in a coach bus with a full police escort and cheering fans three hours before the game, I got off the tram with Bethany and walked up to the stadium without fanfare. Instead of a long line of athletic trainers and physical therapists in the ATR taping ankles on a tight schedule, I stepped into a closet where one AT did his best with what he had.

Thankfully, he soon had extra help. Walking into the stadium, Paul saw me with Bethany and hurried over.

"What's up, guyyys?!" He was in charge of more pre-game logistics than any starting quarterback should be, but took it all in stride.

"Bethany! I'm glad you are here. If you would like, the trainer could use your help, I tell him you will be medical student. This is good for you?"

"Oh! Umm, yeah I'll do my best!"

"Very good, and Tommy, I have some news on the lineup. Brian is sick so he cannot come, so Moose will start at center today. I ask Aadil to play with Division II team so he can help them out. Also, Washnee and Nyor have work today, so they will be here just for the second half. So we will have Sofian start at right guard, and Mamadi at right tackle. Do you think they will be ready?"

Mamadi had raw talent, Moose was old, and Sofian overweight, but they had each been at almost every practice. I'd gladly suit up with them.

"Oh yeah, nous sommes prêts!" [12]

"I love it, let's have some fun toonight!"

It was a beautiful night for football. The sun had set long before our 7:00 PM kickoff, and the low fifties air promised to keep us cool and fresh. Players who need to catch a ball may beg to differ, but I say forty to fifty degrees is the sweet spot for football. We went through our usual warmups, split into individual drills for a few minutes, and returned to the locker room, where a quiet energy hung in the air. Some put in headphones, slowly nodding their heads, others looked at the ground with steely eyes. Niko came in and gave an impassioned speech. No one was around to translate, but I got the point. The time had come, let's do this.

We line up and marched to the mouth of the tunnel. There weren't 100,000 fans, and the sidelines weren't packed with media, staff, and VIPs, but the moment felt just as real. We charged out behind a giant black and yellow flag, jumped around at the fifty for a minute, and then walked back to the sideline for the coin toss. Their ball. They didn't sing *La Marseillaise* before playing. Apparently that was only for playoff games.

I stayed loose on the sideline, anxious to knock out the butterflies. Our defense looked just as good as I'd hoped, and soon the Spartiates lined up to punt. Fourth and eleven. The punt sailed out of bounds and we dashed out to their forty-five yard line.

---

12 *"We are ready!"*

Paul jogged up to the huddle, smiling and ready to have some fun. He winked at James and me.

"Strong gauche, trente-trois action exxon."

Strong right, thirty-three action, got it. We were kicking things off with a play action pass; Paul wanted to be the gunslinger right away.

Settled into my stance, I locked onto the defensive end. Nothing else mattered now. Since it was a play action, I'd come off hard, punch his inside shoulder to sell the run, and then settle into pass protection for as long as Paul needed to throw. They bought the fake and were reading the run for two seconds before they converted to a pass rush. Paul sat back in a picture perfect pocket, gave the receiver a second to get down field, and aired it out. Incomplete, just missed him.

Coming into any game, I have a lot of thoughts. Some of them are meaningful and inspired, others epic and ridiculous. I'm motivated and slightly crazed. But after the first play or two, most of that fades away and my thoughts are a lot simpler. It's like I've cleared my mind of everything but technique, scheme, and aggression. Today was no different. It mattered less that I was in France and more that the defensive end was shifting his weight inside from a tight five technique.

We regrouped in the huddle. Paul said a few words in French to the receiver he'd just targeted, then turned back to the group.

"Ok guyyys. Bunch gauche, trente-trois zone back."

That's more like it.

Inside zone left, right behind James and me. Full back cuts across to take the backside defensive end.

"A plus! Vert cinq.. veeeert cinq-set-hut!"

I fired off the line and the end slanted inside. That made my job easy, since he just took himself away from the play. I pushed him a little further and Guillaume, our hard-nosed running back, took it six yards off of my left hip. Third and four.

Third downs are always key in football. Converting on third down correlates with victory, as any offensive player has been reminded thousands of times.

"Let's get this! Off droit, Houston."

I was hoping for a run, as most offensive linemen typically are, but trusted Paul's arm to make a play.

"Snoop! Snoop! Snoop!" Moose made his call. There are clever pneumonic devices all over a football field, disguising calls from the other team. "Snoop" called to mind, "Snoop Dog," and "dog" started with a D, same as "droit," or, "right." We had a full line slide to the right. I'd leave the defensive end for the running back to cut, and keep an eye on the B gap. James knew he could let anything go that went past him in my direction.

Paul nailed Doukie in the flat [13] for a gain of eight. It started raining, just enough to make it dramatic. We got our run wishes on the next play.

"Off droit open, trente-cinq search."

Thirty-five search, outside zone left. Let's get it.

I zeroed in on the end's outside shoulder. He was tight, so it shouldn't be too hard to reach. This is the kind of block that gets tackles paid in the NFL. Here, I'd settle for the pleasure of doing something well.

"Blue dix, [14] bluuue dix set hut!"

I had the end on his heels after my first punch, and kept driving him back for another ten yards while Guillaume cut back, brushing past my right hip. Their corner dragged him down seven yards later. We were knocking on the red zone's [15] door.

---

13 The area five yards past the line of scrimmage and between the hash and sideline

14 *"Ten"*

15 Inside the twenty yard line

Paul aimed for Doukie across the middle, but the tackle across from Sofian jumped and tipped it. We huddled up, third and three.

Paul looked at the linemen. "Big one here guys, let's go." Then to the group, "Tank gauche, trente-cinq blast."

James and I looked at each other and grinned. *Power left.* Power is almost every offensive lineman's favorite play. It's everything you want to do as a lineman, and none of what you don't. James and I would double team the three technique,[16] bringing our hips and shoulders together to drive him into the backside linebacker's lap.

Just as planned, we created a wave, crashing down on the unsuspecting tackle while Guillaume barreled over all remaining resistance until a safety pushed him out of bounds at the six yard line.

It was first and goal, and Paul called our number again.

"Spread gauche, trentre-deux zone read."

This time Guillaume raced towards Mamadi and Sofian, cut back to the middle, and went down at the four yard line. Second and goal.

We gathered again, exhausted but psyched out. We were so close, like sharks smelling blood in the water.

"Bunch droit, trente-trois zone back." He looked to his Americans. "Punch this in guys!"

And punch it in we did.

Jason, another quick and powerful back, bounced outside and walked in untouched. Touchdown Flash.

James and I both found an extra ounce of energy to jump up and sprint to the celebration in the endzone. With a big crowd, you'd hear a thundering roar after a touchdown. Now, it sounded like a high school game. I could hear individual yells, a drum beating, and a vuvuzela

---

16 The defensive tackle lined up on the guard's outside half

blare. There's something intimate about a crowd like this.

One the sideline, we didn't have game clips to watch or phones ringing from the booth. The offense sat together on benches, laughing and reliving moments from the drive. Paul came over to tell us good job. Moose, Mamadi, and Sofian gave everything they had, and now they drank water, sitting back in satisfied exhaustion.

They wouldn't have long to rest, however, as our defense forced a decisive three and out. [17] The offense gathered together and jogged to our huddle on our own forty-three yard-line to start the next campaign. After confusion amongst the receivers led to a delay of game penalty, pushing us back to our thirty-eight, we marched forward, slowly but surely. Twelve plays, six run and six pass, brought us to the two yard line.

Paul ran up to the huddle, but then gave us a second to catch our breath. Twelve plays will exhaust even the fittest lineman, and neither Moose nor Sofian were guilty of this. None the less, they were resolute and not to be denied.

"Snug doit, trente-trois zone. Finish it boys!"

We leaned forward in our stances. We might as well have told the Spartiates we were running inside zone. James and I came off the ball and cleared space, but Moose made the key block, driving back the nose tackle while Guillaume powered into the endzone behind him. Moose was ecstatic, throwing his hands in the air and picking Guillaume up off the turf.

Our defense did their thing, stuffing the Spartiates behind the line on two straight runs, and dooming a third down pass before it started with a vicious pass rush. Axwel and Gigi were in the quarterback's face before he could look downfield. I was hoping for at least one first

---

17   Three plays without a first down to start a drive

down, if only to give Moose and Sofian a minute to catch their breath.

Unfortunately, our offense showed its first signs of mortality on the next drive, laying an egg with a three and out of our own. Moose and Sofian missed their linebacker on inside zone, Paul hit Doukie across the middle for a nice gain on second down, then we botched the blocking scheme on a short third down.

The Spartiates responded with a nine play drive, capturing their first first-down and advancing to midfield. But it was to no avail. Three hopeless shots at the endzone forced them to punt.

We bounced back in two minute mode, but only made it to midfield when the clock ran out. Flash lead fourteen-zero at the half.

Inside, Washnee and Nyor had arrived and were strapping up their shoulder pads. I greeted them and sat down to grab a water bottle from my backpack. No one came around with trays of drinks, snacks, and supplements. I was getting hungry and made a note to bring something next time.

The second half kicked off fast. Very fast. Stefan, a track star turned wide receiver, caught the opening kickoff, found a seam, and didn't look back.

"Paul you told me he was fast, but you didn't say he was *that* fast." [18] I watched in disbelief as the return team mobbed him in the endzone.

"Yee-ep he can really move."

I threw my helmet on and hustled out for the extra point.

Our defense maintained their dominance, bringing the Spartiates punter back out on fourth and ten. He didn't have a chance to get the kick off, with a herd of Flash bearing down on him, but somehow managed to

---

18   I later timed his 40 yard split on the film and even slowing down at the end, it was a 4.39

scramble left and pick up a first down. Their luck ran out nine plays later, when the panicked quarterback airmailed it out of the endzone on a fourth down effort at the ten. Paul had warned me that French officials like to throw their flags, and that proved true on our next drive, which ate up most of the third quarter. We marched ninety yards down the field, but six penalties slowed the advance. After a flag, the officials would circle together, sometimes for a minute or two, and then address the crowd with the verdict. I didn't understand their calls or bother asking. I figured Paul would tell me if I was guilty of anything serious.

Menacing defensive players like to grab onto your jersey or shoulder pads, even when it serves no practical purpose. I don't know why they do this. Perhaps they know how annoying it is. I'm sure that's it. This bothersome habit made its way to France too. Midway through the drive, I climbed to the backside linebacker on inside zone right. We clashed and I locked onto him. When the ball was away, I turned to chase down Guillaume, but the little French man was gripping the front of my jersey. Anger can be irrationally amplified when you're exhausted and this made me furious. I pushed him back once, but he held on. I shouted to let go, but he either didn't understand or didn't care. *A slight smirk??* I raised my arm and brought down a karate chop with everything I had, aiming for his forearm. Instead of a violent collision that would knock this zebra mussel off once and for all, I swung through air, stumbling forward. He jogged away, laughing, with another Spartiate. *Touché.*

Paul finally ended the drive with a twenty-yard touchdown pass to Stefan, cutting across the middle. I made sure the coast was clear of flags and dutifully pumped my fist in the air, jogging to my spot on the field goal unit.

Any backups we had went in, and not much happened after that. I did my best to keep an eye on Maha, a newbie from the Division II team who backed me up at left tackle. He looked very lean and very lost. Something to work on.

When the clock ran out, we shook hands in the customary line across the fifty, and then thanked the officials, who stood together on the forty-five. I thought that was a nice touch. Officiating may be a great way to stay in the game when you're older, but I couldn't hold down a job as a ref. In my distorted disdain for the defense, I'd never call an offensive holding.

Niko congratulated us on a win, reminding us that we had a long season ahead and a heck of a lot to get better at. When we broke it down, we didn't run to the locker room to talk to the media, but scattered across the field to pick everything up. Who else would do it? I grabbed two pylons from the North endzone. Mamadi and Moose shuffled towards the shed with a bench. Many hands made light work and we had the operation complete in minutes.

Bethany was standing on the sideline, next to some of her new friends from the women's team. My heart fluttered, seeing her smiling in the light rain, wearing a Flash jacket that made her look even smaller than she already was.

"Bon travail monsieur!" She attempted in her most dignified French.

"Ahh, merci beaucoup madame!" I replied before giving her kiss.

"Did you have fun? It looked like you were having fun." She observed with a grin.

"Yeah, yeah that was pretty good. Winning was nice too."

"I felt a lot more relaxed watching you than the last time."

We laughed, thinking of how far we'd come from running onto Soldier Field, wondering if I'd get fired when cuts came around the next day.

I did have fun playing today. I was already full of pride for the Flash. I played hard and felt like I contributed. I know the Spartiates aren't the best France has to offer, not by a long shot. But it was a good start. The first step. As much as ever before, I don't want to look ahead. It's not like I'm here to earn some next step – this is it.

I felt good. I wonder if we don't want to admit that we feel good, because then we're supposed to perform. If we didn't feel good to begin with, we have an excuse if we don't do well, and a great story if we do. The most pain I felt today was when I tore every last hair off of my foot and ankle in the locker room after the game. Apparently pre wrap [19] isn't a part of French taping doctrine. I'd shave my ankle next time if there were anything left to remove.

Afterwards in the locker room, Marcus invited us to grab a drink. We walked over to his locker. A circle of half-dressed victors danced to rhythmic music. He poured a Dixie cup half full of Captain Morgan and mixed in some Ginger Ale. I hope that always reminds me of today.

I took the tram back with Bethany and James, reliving great plays and pancakes [20] from the game. James played hard and physical, it was fun to watch. In addition to being a great player, he's easygoing and fun to be around.

Back in Stade de Mode, I made potato wedges and beef ravioli with chicken on the side. I covered the ravioli in olive oil, butter, garlic seasoning, and pepper. Two wins in one night! Next I made something that convinced

19 A thin layer of foam tape designed to prevent exactly this issue

20 When you knock the defender flat on his back, flat like a pancake

me I never needed to spend more than a Euro to enjoy dessert – sweet bread with Patamilka and whipped cream. Wonderful! Why would I need any more than that? We called my Mom afterwards for her birthday and talked about the game. I was touched to hear from family and friends who had tuned into the livestream.

Few outside of the stadium cared who won, but that was okay.

Coach Niko addressing us the night before game one.

CHAPTER IV

Molosses

Sunday, February 2, 2020 – Super Bowl Abroad

Bethany finished her makeup in the bathroom and I told James we'd be in the hallway in a minute. It was 9:30 PM and our night was about to start. Early tomorrow morning was the greatest spectacle in sports. Thousand-dollar nose bleed seats and million-dollar commercial slots. A mammoth clash of titans that brought the masses together for wings, advertisements, and some football. I'm talking, of course, about the Super Bowl. However, we were in Europe, and the game wasn't etched into the cultural fabric. Here, the Super Bowl felt more like a cult classic. I've scoffed at friends of mine who wake up at ungodly hours to watch international soccer matches and yet, here I was, preparing to spend most of the night watching people my age play a game in a different country. I was one of *those* guys. Fortunately, I knew the rest of *those* guys in northeast Paris, and we were getting together to watch the game.

Brian invited the offensive line to his apartment, and was feeling well enough to stick to the plan. Aadil, who doesn't live far from us, offered to drive. James, Bethany, and I piled into Aadil's small stick shift, pretending we didn't notice the drowsiness setting in already. Kickoff was at 12:30 AM and this game could take four hours, so we'd need to rally.

We drove for another thirty minutes away from the city. A winter mix came into view whenever we drove under streetlights. In the United States, driving away from a city-center follows a more or less predictable pattern. The business district gives way apartments, which get shorter until they turn into single-family homes. The houses and yards get bigger and the strip malls less frequent until you see a farm, and you've reached rural America. Following this script, Souilly should have been suburban flirting with rural, but instead looked like a quaint mid-city neighborhood uprooted from Paris and transplanted an hour away. The streets were quiet as we circled the sloped blocks looking for parking. Brian stuck his head out of a second story window and called instructions down to Aadil in a hushed tone, careful not to create a disturbance this late. Fluttering snowflakes drifted quietly to the ground.

The buzzer welcomed us into an open air stairwell with Brian waiting at the top.

"Hi guys, thanks for coming. Good job with the win last night, sorry I can't be there."

"Thanks for having us, are you feeling better?"

"Yes much better, I am just mad to not be there."

"Yeah bro we got you, we held it down. Moose didn't make the calls like you do though." James added.

"Oh yes thank you and speaking of Moose, he says he cannot come tonight, and I don't know of Mamadi and Sofian. Washnee and Nyor have work tonight so they don't come. I hope you are hungry, because it will just be us, even though I cook for many more. Come, we can go inside."

The one-bedroom apartment was warm and inviting. I thought of countless apartments on the north end of Chicago, with hardwood floors, a modern kitchen, and exposed brick. Homes paint a picture of a person. The space was humble but well kept, decorated with Madagascan artifacts, a Flash poster, and pictures with his girlfriend at her equestrian competitions. Their spiced candle was overpowered by a wave of mouth-watering smells coming from the kitchen.

Brian and his girlfriend had gone all out for the party and showed remarkable hospitality. They served chicken wings, steak burgers, homemade onion rings, and a tray of vegetables carefully arranged around a dipping bowl. We discovered Samurai sauce, made of mayonnaise, ketchup, and a Tunisian chili paste. I put it on everything we had and intend to continue doing so for the remainder of my life.

"James you could put this stuff on the Guilt Trip. You know I'm gonna visit Long Island and we're going there, right?"

"Bro make it happen. There's more than *just* that I gotta show you on LI though, like they got this one called the Surf and Turf, with fried shrimp and stuff in it with all the real meat."

"Well we will see how much Americans can really eat tonight, since no one else comes you must eat it all." Brian challenged us.

Brian's girlfriend wished us goodnight and turned in. She had better things to do throughout the night, like sleeping.

We ate, talked, and watched a French dubbed NCIS-LA episode while we waited for kickoff. I heard scratching behind the bedroom door, and Brian stepped away from the steak burgers to open it. Out burst a lean brown dog! It ran a lap around the apartment, noticed it had company, and eagerly welcomed us with a tennis ball.

"This is Cavalier, she is a German Pointer and loves to play fetch. Be careful or she will make you play all night."

Bethany took the offering and sent Cavalier barreling across the living room, grabbing the ball and striding in place like the roadrunner until she found enough traction on the hardwood floor to bring it back. The process repeated itself until Bethany respectfully excused herself from Cavalier's propositions.

12:30 came and it was time for kickoff. We turned to the French broadcast, put on by two former Flash players. I watched the Forty-Niners and the Chiefs run from the tunnel into Hard Rock Stadium in Miami, the same stadium I ran into six months ago with the Falcons. Four years ago, battling Ohio State in the Horseshoe, I held my own against Nick Bosa. Then a true Freshman, he was full of raw talent and living in his older brother's shadow. We weren't just peers, I was the veteran all-conference lineman from the Big Ten West. It was strange seeing him now, the defensive rookie of the year, unfathomably wealthy and leading his team in the Super Bowl. I guess I should have been jealous of him, but was just happy to be sitting there in Souilly.

You're just telling yourself that to make it hurt less. Of course you'd rather be rich and playing in the Super Bowl. Don't be ridiculous.

How can you look around and wish you were somewhere else? You're free, on an adventure. Never meeting these guys or eating this food? No thanks.

You were good enough, at least to make a practice squad. Admit it. You got screwed when they kept cutting you and never really gave you a chance. You could just pay for a

*flight to Paris if you were making that kind of money. You'd
be verified on Twitter too.*

    But what can I do now?

    You were good enough. You should be rich.

    Shut up!!

    The thoughts went back and forth while I watched
the first few drives. I chose to ignore the debate. It had
been raging in my head for months and there was no
settling it.

    It made sense that James and I would be awake
right now, but how did Frenchmen from Seychelles and
Madagascar end up throwing this party? If nothing else,
they had to leave for work in a few hours.

    "So Brian, Aadil, how did you guys learn about
and start playing football?"

    "I had a friend invite me to his practice and saw
them play. I know then that I want to play this game."
Aadil answered first.

    "What did you see that you liked about it?"

    "Oh um, well it was like a family, the team. And
it has many types of people. Different size and different,
um, *role* to play. But still they were important. It was a
hard thing to do and I wonder if I could do it."

    I looked at Brian.

    "It's the same thing man, I have a friend invite
me to practice. I was not fast enough for soccer, but I
see I can do things as lineman in football. Then I love
the culture of football too."

    We spent the next three hours enjoying the fanfare,
stuffed to capacity with Brian's hospitality. I've never
watched football at 3:30 AM before, and started to fade
until an electric fourth quarter comeback woke us up and
crowned the Chiefs Super Bowl champions. The late night
resynced us with American time zones, and we kept in
touch with friends and family back home, including my

dad who was working at the game. He walked through the security line behind Cardi B.

My dad is the sports director for WOOD-TV 8, the NBC affiliate in West Michigan. He's covered every major event in sports, including eleven Olympic games. I was always around sports growing up, and looking at sports through my dad's eyes taught me to see more than just exercise and entertainment. Sports develop and expose character while providing an arena for human stories to play out. It was unscripted, yet compelling beyond anything Hollywood could concoct. Asked his favorite athlete he's interviewed and he won't tell you Jordan, Woods, or Jeter, but Joe Burmania, a double-amputee Paralympic basketball player. His Emmy awards are hidden behind books in the corner of his office.

I had a lot to learn from him when the media took interest in what I had to say as a high school recruit. First lesson – the funny thoughts you like to share with your friends aren't the right ones for a phone interview. For whatever reason, there are enough people interested in what fifteen-year-old boys have to say to bankroll numerous recruiting blogs and reporters. In my first interview with such a site, the reporter asked me if I'd like to visit other schools or if I'd just accept the Michigan offer I just received.

Heck I don't know, I thought I wanted to go to the Coast Guard Academy last week. Hey, this one got a rouse out of the older guys at church who asked me the same question yesterday.

"Well I'll probably look around a little more, maybe I'll check out West Point, or take a visit to Hawaii just for the all-expense paid trip."

My dad overheard this burgeoning debacle and rushed into the room, desperately gesturing for me to shut up.

"You think Hawaii will ever want to talk to you if they hear that? Be a real person and show your personality, but think about how other people will hear the things you say." He suggested after I hung up.

Bethany and James slept on the ride home, while Aadil and I rehashed the game. He dropped us off around 5:30 AM so that we could sleep the morning away while he hurried back to his apartment to get ready for work.

Monday, February 3, 2020 – The Film

As the official after action review, post-game film sessions are a big deal. Before the get together, everyone should have watched the film at least once and reviewed the coach's comments and grade sheet. The plays the group watches together either focus on correcting mistakes or highlighting wins. It could be a grand time reliving great plays, or the most stressful hour of your week.

We sat in Paul's small office and got down to business.

"So what did you guys think of the first game?"

"It was calm, our defense is *mad* good. I know we're gonna put some more points up. You see me and Tommy wreckin dudes out there?"

"Yeah you guys play very good. I still am pissed off at some of my throws. I don't know how I miss Doukie on curl near the twenty in the second quarter. Buuuut I guess it was game number one, we get better."

"Bro Paul you gotta teach me some new French words, these dudes were jawin at me all game and I'm just like screamin 'I DON'T KNOW WHAT YOU'RE SAYING' but they didn't really care."

"Tommy you learning French, did you talk some trash on Saturday?"

"Ahh, that's never really been my speciality, besides it's not on DuoLingo."

"I see I see. Well, we can watch some plays. Moose and Sofian play hard I think, but Moose is slow and Sofian also, and Mamadi does not know what to do."

He fumbled with the WI-FI for a few minutes and gave up.

"Well, you can see the film later. I have some ideas for a play."

Paul jumped up and scribbled on the whiteboard.

"I think we have good speed to use with the receivers, and I want that you can block in space. So we slide right and have you two release for linebacker and safety." He looked at his watch and cursed.

"I have to go coach the junior quarterbacks, you can finish the film if you like. I will see you tomorrow. Take care to lock the door when you leave." He jogged down the hall to go build up the next generation of French football players.

James and I mostly wanted to watch our pancakes from the game, but the single camera angle never stayed on the linemen long enough to see it. We decided to call it a night.

Tuesday, February 4, 2020 – Uncle Steve

On the night of February 1, 1992, Troopers Steven Niewiek and James DeLoach responded to an officer in distress. En route, their squad car was struck by a train, killing Trooper DeLoach immediately. Trooper Niewiek was pulled from the car by good Samaritans and rushed to the hospital, where he died in surgery early the next morning.

My full name, Thomas Steven Doles, remembers Trooper Niewiek, better known as Uncle Steve. My parents were engaged when he died, but in some ways I feel like I knew him. Stories of his gregarious love and sense of justice shaped me. This morning, I found myself thinking about him, two days after the twenty-eighth anniversary of his death. Thinking about the fifty-three year-old uncle I could have had. I scrolled through a memorial forum online, reading reflections from friends, family, and fellow officers. I've seen this page before and posted on it myself, but this morning I found something that made me pause.

Big Steve,

I can still hear your voice in the back of the ambulance. I held your hand and asked where you were hurting. You told me that only your arm was hurting.... I will never forget that. I remember handing you off the POH doctors and then we cleared the hospital thinking you were going to surgery and then it would be OK. Getting that telephone call the next morning and they told us that you did not make it. My heart sank that morning and still does to this present day.

I just had to share that thought. R.I.P my brotha...

Firefighter-EMT Ryan Gross
Waterford Regional Fire Department
May 11, 2014

Tears started to well up in my eyes. That night had always been a story that might as well have happened in a different world. Maybe I protected myself emotionally by thinking about it abstractly. I saw the deep wounds the tragedy had cut into my family and found it easier to consider his heroism from afar. But hearing from the

EMT who held his hand in the ambulance? It forced me to get closer to his pain than I ever had before.

Out of curiosity, I searched for Ryan Gross on Facebook. Sure enough, there he was, still serving the Waterford Township Fire Department. I sent him a message, thanking him for sharing that memory, and for the work he does as a first responder. He replied not long after.

Hi Mr. Doles. I am the same Firefighter that was on the scene. It's a day I will never forget and I am sorry for your family's loss.

I thought of how different our family might be if he survived. What other cousins I might have, and what my relationship with him would be like. I thought about his age when he died. Just months older than me. I wasn't sure if it made him younger, or me older. It seemed impossible that twenty-four years was enough to leave such a legacy. I wiped away another tear and looked at Bethany sleeping next to me. A beautiful, godly, loving wife. Why was I already enjoying gifts of this life that Uncle Steve never tasted? Was football and my journey to France living the kind of life that would leave a legacy?

Only in the hope of the Gospel do I see light enter this tragedy, but the light is bright. I have hope that Uncle Steve's death was our loss and his gain. That there will be a long awaited reunion someday. I really believe this. That there will be an eternity of fellowship and love, free of the sinful hinderances clinging to us on earth. Surpassing anything we could hope for in this life. Safe in the arms of the savior who makes this hope possible.

Wednesday, February 5, 2020 – Bastille

"Yo Tommy, you and Bethany wanna go into Paris? I figured we could check some stuff out since we don't got practice and stuff."

"Yeah we'd be down, we were thinking of going to see the Catacombs, would you wanna do that?"

"The Caaaaatacombs? Bro I don't know about *that.*"

"Didn't you say your buddy called that was his favorite thing in the city?"

"Yeah but this guy was crazy. Totally into weird stuff like that."

"So stacked up bones aren't really your thing?"

He laughed sheepishly and scratched his head. "Bro I'm low key scared of that stuff, I don't even like *looking* at cemeteries, or even pictures of them. But I guess if you guys wanna go I'm in."

We rode Tram One north to metro Line Five and headed towards *Bastille.* We had room to sit down in the train and we spent the thirty minute ride talking on and off. James usually had a white earbud fed through his green and yellow Long Island hoodie, the tinselly beat of a rap song playing for the room to hear. But he was always open to conversation when invited.

"James do you have any brothers or sisters?" Bethany asked.

"Yeah I got two sisters, both older."

"Nice, are you guys pretty close?"

"Ahh, yeah kinda. More than we used to be. Man, I was *nuts* when I was a kid, and they weren't really about it. Like my sisters were chillin until I was born but I came along and would just run around stuff nonstop. I didn't even talk until I was like five but like I didn't need to cuz I would just point at stuff and my sisters would do it cuz they were scared of me. But yeah now we're all pretty cool."

We arrived in the early afternoon, deposited squarely in *Place de Bastille*. Built in the fourteenth century to fend off the British during the Hundred Years War, the Bastille really made a name for itself during the French Revolution. It was a fortified state prison until, on July 14, 1789, an angry mob stormed the prison. They freed a mere seven prisoners, but more importantly, captured a symbol of despotic monarchial power. Now, a tall green pillar known as *Colonne de Juillet*[1] stood to commemorate France's revolutionary spirit.

"Imagine if you had my magic time glasses, the things you could see right here!"

"Yeah that would be cool. I don't know. This is cool to see and all, but unless you're going to geek out about magic time glasses, there's not that much to do once you've looked at it."

"I guess that's true." I replied, looking across the square at James, who was content watching an anime episode on his phone.

Fortunately, there was plenty else to see nearby. We walked west down *Rue Saint-Antoine* to the *Place des Vosges*, a perfectly square plaza surrounded by matching brick-façade mansions, side by side. Everything was symmetrical, from the exterior features of the buildings to the trees and fountains in the garden. We walked through the pedestrian arcades and dreamed of a leisurely spring afternoon here.

There are things you see in Europe that just don't exist in the United States, nor should we ever expect them to. I thought of the unique arcs of history that had to converge in the seventeenth century for this beautiful plaza to exist. A single family needed to concentrate enough political and economic power that anything

---

1 *July Column*

they desired would come to be. This family needed to desire a massive display of French Baroque architecture to impress their friends. Technology must have been in place to make their wish possible.

When we stepped out of the next metro station, there was very little to indicate we were near one of the city's most famous landmarks. The Catacombs are, of course, underground. Beneath the trappings of daily life and even the metro lines. We came to a small storefront where we paid for admission and proceeded to the spiral staircase that would lead us sixty-meters into the underworld.

On the way down, the snooty British man narrating the audio tour informed me that underground Paris was full of sprawling limestone quarries. As the population began to grow in the eighteenth century, space was at a premium and the powers that be decided church parishes shouldn't take acres of prime real estate to house the remains of long-dead plague victims. Instead, they'd take them downstairs, where there was plenty of room. Nightly processions carted unearthed bones to the ossuaries underground, trailed by chanting priests to cover any undead curse liabilities.

The best word to describe the sight was *macabre*. Neatly stacked bones lined the walls. There was enough light to find your way, but not much more. It was spooky, but intriguing. Inviting reflection on mortality and wonder over the lives these skulls must have lived. It called to mind *The Cask of Amontillado*, *Coco*, Ezekiel 37, my cousin's childhood Halloween haunted houses, and Scooby Doo. Walking into the main ossuary, an engraved stone warns you - *Arret, c'est ici l'empire de la morte.* [2]

We weren't the first ones to be chilled and enchanted by this morbid labyrinth. In 1897, one hundred or so members of Parisian high society received a secret invitation to enter the empire of the dead under the

2   *"Stop, this is the empire of the dead."*

cloak of darkness. When they arrived at the candle-lit enclave, a group of musicians satisfied everyone's lurid lusts, playing the night away with tunes such as Chopin's *Funeral March* and Camille Saint-Saens' *Danse Macabre*.

Walking down here will turn anyone's attention to mortality, and I was no different, climbing the stairs back to the surface. The bedrock of my worldview is the existence of a holy, loving, and just God. Every human has rebelled against this good God, bringing eternal punishment on his own head. The story doesn't end there, for God himself bore the punishment we deserved, such that faith in him spares us from wrath. I believe every skull I walked past today represents a soul that lives on. I rest in peace believing that my body's return to dust won't mark the end of my soul.

The dizzying spiral stairs opened into a gift shop, selling all manner of creepy curiosities. James was in the corner, examining a skull keychain and bone pen.

"How long have you been up here?"

"Bro I flew through that. It was cool ya know, but *mad* creepy. I guess this gift shop isn't much better, but at least the skulls aren't real!"

Thursday, February 6, 2020 – We Colonized You

James and I were walking to the tram after practice and saw Marco, the new linebacker from London, walking in the same direction. We caught up and walked with him the rest of the way. After hearing about his transition to Paris, we stood in the cool glow of the platform.

"Bro, your English is pretty good, I'm impressed with it." James complimented.

"My English? I did mention I was from London, no?"

"Yeah but like, I thought you'd speak *British* there."

I perked up and Marco seemed unsure he'd heard him right.

"British? I don't.. Um, London... *England*. English.. I.. we colonized you mate, remember? That's why you speak English."

Marco looked over to me, making sure he wasn't losing it.

I raised my hands and eyebrows, shaking my head. Not much I could say about that one but chalk it up to fatigue, a cross-cultural morass, and perhaps some innocent naiveté.

***

A lot of people in America care what football players are doing and have to say. After a game, I'd give my perspective on how things went and what it meant for the season. Northwestern wanted to promote the Wildcat brand, and told us to capture the most interesting things we did on social media. Sometimes they even provided the camera. The "platform" that athletes love to talk about is real, but as often as it's used for good, it's used to feed our egos.

In France, no one cares that I play football. This forces me to wrestle with some questions I haven't for a while. Where is the joy when you're not packaging experiences and shipping them out to anyone who will listen?[3] What do we lose when we toil in obscurity? What do we gain?

More so than French football, marriage is teaching me to enjoy the beauty in moments I'll never share publicly. Whether it would be inappropriate or just wouldn't make sense, the best things in my life now can't be shared with anyone but Bethany. And this is enough! It frees me to give voice to an inexplicable alter ego in the kitchen

---

3 On some level, is that what this book is doing?

without worrying about how to explain it online. To cry laughing over a joke I don't remember. To solve the world's problems during pillow talk. Contentment is a gift.

Another threat to contentment has been worrying about the future. This temporary fairytale will end someday, less than six months from now. Life will go on. Finishing dinner after practice, these worries floated to the front of my mind. *Where will you live? What will you do in East Tennessee? How will you pay for medical school?* Walking back from the kitchen, I saw the faint beam of the Eifel Tower sweep across the cold night sky. *I shouldn't wait to enjoy the present until there aren't any uncertainties about the future. That will never happen.*

Friday, February 7, 2020 – Verdun

Mariannick handed over the keys and warned us about speed radars. With a bye this weekend, we were hitting the road. Badis had to work and couldn't join, but Bethany, James, and I had plotted a trip to Luxembourg. We booked an Airbnb and had a few ideas, but the itinerary was wide open. James got a playlist going and we gleefully headed east on A4.

The apartments, stores, and factories of Paris gave way to a truly beautiful countryside. Passing through Champaign, idyllic villages were nestled between rolling green hills and patches of trees. The sun shined through sparse clouds and I felt as relaxed as I have in a while. From a distance, it didn't look like the small towns had changed much in two hundred years. A single quaint steeple standing over a cluster of stone cottages. As if on cue, a silent bullet train blew past us and disappeared into the hills, reminding us we *were* in the twenty-first century.

Our first stop would be Verdun, the infamous World War I battlefield. In February 1916, the German Fifth Army attacked French fortifications on the Western Front near Verdun. What ensued was the longest and second deadliest battle in human history.[4] Over the course of ten months, both sides dug in. Attacks and counterattacks continued under shell filled skies while reinforcements replaced the rapidly accumulating casualties. The German strategy was attrition: to "bleed the French army white" and turn their attention to Great Britain. Over 700,000 men died.

Driving through the solemn woods towards the battlefield, we stopped talking and looked outside, trying to feel the weight of this place. One of the bloodiest and most hellish scenes the world had ever seen, a high point of human misery. The application of industrialization to the destruction of man. I could hardly wrap my head around it. Millions of screaming artillery shells raining death from the sky, day and night? Thousands of young men, delivered to these hills from all corners of France and Germany, killed daily? In a clearing next to the road, about the size of a highway rest stop, a marker told the story of sixty-thousand Nazis armed with flame throwers advancing on a bunker from the hill beneath us. Thousands dead, right where we stood. Wounded soldiers choking on poisonous gas.

How do you even imagine something like that? It registered in my head, but I thought that if I could *feel* it, I'd break down sobbing. Perhaps distance created the emotional barrier. At an American battlefield, I think about the towns the men came from. The schools they went to and the books they read. I feel a sense of comradery and appreciation for their sacrifice. Here, we were a few steps removed.

---

4 The deadliest, Stalingrad, also came on the heels of an attempted German invasion, this time into the Soviet Union

We parked near the *Douaumont* Ossuary, a tubular concrete structure entrusted with the skeletal remains of 13,000 unidentified French and German soldiers. Peeking through a small window near the ground, a cobwebbed skull looked back at me. For not liking cemeteries, James sure was putting up with a lot in a few days. Inside, the sun shined through orange windows, lighting the chamber with an ethereal amber glow. We climbed to the top of the forty-six meter tower for panoramic views of the battlefield.

The peace of today was hard to reconcile with the carnage that once reigned. One hundred years ago we'd have found a rotting lunar landscape. The brutal haze of death and destruction. But today? A cool, gentle breeze flowing through leafless trees was the only sound. The grass was green and the sky was blue. Nature had mended the wounds left by the brokenness of man. Patches of orchids and small ponds full of newts. But there were still scars. The ground was mangled and jagged, unnatural divots betraying ceaseless shelling. Abandoned fortifications dotted the landscape.

Outside, rows of white crosses remembered the dead who *could* be identified. The crosses kept going, row after row. But each a life! A soul! I said a prayer for peace on earth and strolled through, looking at the names and dates. Growing up, soldiers seemed like distant heroes. Wise, grown, experienced, and mature. Looking at these crosses, however, I didn't even see my peers, but my juniors! Seventeen and eighteen year-old boys who barely had the chance to be men! Why did I get to live into my twenties without being drafted into war? Why wasn't I sent over the edge of a bunker into certain death?

I thought about the confidence I had that my son would never meet such a fate and wondered if it was merited. How much faith should I have in democratic peace theory? Mutually assured destruction? Changing tactics?

The United Nations? The European Union? American hegemony? What was really protecting me from a similar fate? Was anything? I said another prayer for peace.

None of us said much walking around the battlefield. Eventually James lost interest and Bethany was ready to go. They patiently waited while I moseyed my way through yet another concrete fort. The sun was getting low and I didn't want to be here alone after dark.

"Well, you guys ready for Luxembourg?"

***

With the sun setting on Verdun, we drove through Belgium and to our Airbnb in Goesdorf, Luxembourg. As easily as going from Michigan to Indiana, we were traveling internationally. Driving at night was enchanting. Narrow roads wound around castle topped hills. Germanic influence presented itself in half-timber houses and streets named *Rindfleischetikettierungsüberwachungsaufgabenübertragungsgesetz.* [5]

We pulled up to a charming old farmhouse in a wooded hollow around 7:00 PM. A kind, middle-aged Dutchman named Allard welcomed us at the front door and led us to our rooms on the second floor. Walking up the spiral stairs, a bearlike dog came around the corner, pounced on Allard and started thrusting against his leg. He playfully brushed her off.

"Usually I ask that they would buy me dinner first."

I paused for a second, wondering what might have been lost in translation. I saw a smile forming from the side of his mouth and realized that's exactly what I was supposed to hear. We had a funny guy.

---

5 You may have guessed that I didn't see a street sign with this written on it. However, it is a real word, meaning, "the law for the delegation of monitoring beef labeling."

"So Allard, how long have you lived here?" Bethany asked.

"Oh me? I just lived here for a few years now. My wife her family lives here since three hundred years now. We still keep the farm, but make most money with the rooms."

"Three *hundred* years! So does your wife do much farming?"

"Oh yes, she can care for the farm, but she is musician also and travels for dis. She speak seven languages you know."

Just when I thought living on a tenth generation farm meant you had a small world.

After settling in, we said hello to some cows behind the barn and climbed back into the car, by now desperately ready for supper. We drove along a rushing river and pulled up to what looked like a hunting lodge from ages past.

Inside, we found an oak table under a low-arched brick ceiling. Animal heads kept an eye on the patrons and chains of sausages hung behind the bar across the room. Luxembourg sat at a crossroads in Europe, and the menu was printed in French, German, English, and Luxembourgish. I don't remember saying anything when we walked in, but the friendly young waitress greeted us in English.

"Velcome to AM Keller, vat would you like to eat toonite?" She asked, placing a tray of bread, olives, and butter on our table.

"Hi, the *Goulash Giebel* looks fun, what kind of meat is in it?" I was intrigued.

"Ah, vell, dis is..." She spit a string of German across the room to a group of old men drinking from beer steins at the bar. One of them shouted back immediately, but the other two heard his answer and forcefully objected. The three of them hollered at each other, and with more vitriol than could reasonably be expected for the situation. They turned away from us and kept going.

"Vell, dis is vild schvein. Very good, you vill like." She vas right. My hearty goulash was covered in salty gravy and absolutely hit the spot. As I delicately placed a radish on the next chunk of boar, I noticed Bethany giving me a familiar look.

"Bro for a big guy you don't eat very fast." James must have seen the same thing. His plate was already clean.

"Well, I order a lot of food and usually talk too much."

"That's definitely true, but you're also a psychopath sometimes, in the nicest way." Bethany nodded at the carefully arranged radishes.

"Hmm. Maybe you've got a point. I like to enjoy my meals. Guilty!"

Bethany and James insisted they had enjoyed their meals just as well, and in less than twenty-minutes.

"Listen, I'm not just gonna hork it down like a *swine!*"

The old men at the bar looked over. I smiled at them and turned away.

"Besides," I could hardly take my argument seriously anymore, but kept it going to stall for more time, "now that I don't have a team feeding me all the time, I have to savor everything I can get."

"Bro I don't know about that but I'll tell you what, when you come over for The Guilt Trip sometime, you're gonna have to hurry up or you will *literally* be there all day. At *least.*"

We called it a night and drove back to the barn, tiptoeing past the excitable dog on our way upstairs. Lying in bed, I furiously scanned Wikipedia articles, brushing up on my European history while Bethany futilely skipped between French, German, and Luxembourgish greetings on DuoLingo. Warm cedar planks lined the wall. Outside, the river rushed and a cow mooed. Having arrived in the dark, I had no picture of the surrounding landscape in my head, but that only added to the magic of it.

Saturday, February 8, 2020 – Castle on a Hill

I heard the faint rush of water running outside. Rubbing my eyes, I slid out of bed, careful not to wake Bethany, and walked towards the early-morning light streaming into the room. I wiped some light condensation off of the window and looked outside. A light fog still obscured the tops of the hills around us, but I could see the stream cutting through a ravine, babbling against small rocks on its way to lower ground. The ground was green but the trees showed no signs of spring. A few cream-colored cows nonchalantly chewed grass together, gossiping about the latest motley crew to show up at their barn. I was hungry too.

Allard had made it abundantly clear he wouldn't be awake when we left, but did stock the fridge in the shared kitchen space last night. It was packed with more glass food containers than we could hope to go through. Yogurt, cheeses, deli meats, fruit, juices. James emerged in pleated black sweatpants and a gray Adidas windbreaker while I set the table. I heard Bethany getting ready in our room.

While we sat down to put a dent in Allard's generous spread, I pulled up a map on my phone to plot a course for the day.

"I know we said it would be cool to see a castle. We could go to Vianden Castle, like forty-minutes from here, and then go from there to Luxembourg City, another forty-five minutes south and towards Paris."

"A castle sounds tight, let's do it."

Outside, the morning air energized me. A day free for adventure - just what we hoped for! I took a look around before getting back in the car. The farmhouse fit precisely into the setting. The chipped mortar washed brick suggested charm and character, but not disrepair. Four cows looked at us blankly while they chewed. *Ignorant simpletons.*

We zipped along narrow winding roads. This was the old country, but the landscape left plenty of hints that it was still the world's fourth richest per capita.[6] A bright red Ferrari whipped around a bend, almost hitting us, and we had to slow down for a futuristic city bus servicing the small farm town we were passing through.

Bethany was enchanted by the countryside.

"Ooo look how cute that farm is! Maybe I could be the rural doctor for this town and we could live here. You can be like Allard, a crude Dutchman who runs an Airbnb!"

"You know, I've heard worse ideas."

With no hope of citing a source, I've heard that happiness correlates with an ability to enjoy what a cynic might call 'cheesiness.' The more pleasure you can find in, say, a renaissance festival, the more pleased you'll be with life in general. If this theory is any more than a nerd's justification for playing Settlers of Catan, I ought to have tenure on cloud nine. My point is, I cannot overstate how excited I was to see a castle.

We paid for the audio tour and perused the courtyards, halls, towers, and chambers of Vianden Castle. Perched high atop a bluff in the Ardennes Mountains,

---

6 $114,705 GDP per capita according to the World Bank (2019), Trailing Monaco ($185,829), Liechtenstein ($181,403), and Bermuda ($117,089). The United States ranks 13th at ($65,297). For context, however, one might remember the top earners are very small and mostly tax havens. The United States GDP is $21.43 trillion compared to Monaco's $7.2 billion.

the fortress looked down on a quiet town below. Before artillery rendered castles useless, I can't imagine how any disgruntled neighbors could have taken down the king of the hill.

The castle had been restored to its medieval glory. In a time before electricity, gas, internet, and plumbing, the nobles who roamed these halls lived in as much comfort and elegance as they could hope for. An ornate fireplace warmed the imposing dining room, with a long wooden table surrounded by paintings of past lords. Imagine the room full of nobles, discussing matters of state with a drumstick of meat in one hand and a chalice of chocolate milk in the other while knights kept watch from the towers above!

The kitchen was fun. A massive spit hung above a fireplace, ready to rotate any number of unlucky wild animals. I like to believe this was how they cooked my goulash last night. Bethany was beside herself at the sight of an oversized wooden spice cart that would have immediately made our registry if sold at Bed Bath and Beyond.

While life certainly wasn't as glamorous for the commoners working in the castle, our favorite room was their space in the basement. Oak barrels of ale were stacked from floor to vaulted ceiling in the social hall, which looked like the inspiration for all things 'dilly-dilly.'

James again found his way through the many rooms faster than we did, but was patiently waiting in the gift shop, buying an Excalibur key chain to add to his budding collection. With a few more pictures, we were off.

"Guys it would only add a little bit of time if we drove into Germany on our way, what do you think?"

So our international travel continued. Luxembourg eased us into the Franco-Germanic culture change, but driving over the Our River, there was no doubt we were in Germany. In actuality, very little changed, but we were convinced we'd driven into the heart of Bavaria.

"Look, a German restaurant!"
"A German car!"
"A German field!"
"A German fox! In the field!"

Overwrought observations aside, we did notice more protestant churches, a Jägermeister bar, and had to turn from *Echternacherbrück* onto *Huttingen bei Lahr* which of course merged with *Niedergeckler*. As an American accustomed to seeing a flag in every front yard, I was surprised to see very few German flags. Germany is widely admired for its collective acceptance of responsibility for atrocities committed in the twentieth century, and I suspect that impacts their circumspect relationship with patriotism.

I got curious about German Americans. The largest single ethnic group in the United States, with over forty-four million claiming roots, yet it seemed hidden. Why? According to a Wikipedia [7] article on German Americans, this was not always the case. Germans used to proudly showcase their culture. Restaurants, parades, associations, etc. They spoke the language in many churches and schools. The author compared German to Spanish in the 21st century, an unofficial second language. So what happened? Two world wars. When Germany became the hated enemy of the free world not once but twice, the German cultural status was irreparably damaged. Immigrants would acknowledge only their other European roots or make one up. They stopped speaking German in public. Whereas the Japanese could be excluded from American life because of their looks, Germans had the option to assimilate, so they did.

---

7   Take it or leave it!

We took a wrong turn and ended up in Arendelle from Frozen. Architecturally uniform houses, churches, offices, and castle structures wound around a small mountain. Towering brick viaduct bridges connected sections of the city across gorges, but most traffic opted for a sleek steel suspension bridge. Luxembourg City seemed to face a classic European dilemma – how to preserve a unique past while adapting and competing in the future? Glass banks and corporate headquarters either hid amongst the fairy-tale or were relegated to the other side of the river.

We found parking and set out on a walk. When I saw someone, I wasn't sure if I should attempt my French, give a greeting in German, or admit I knew no Luxembourgish. It seemed like signs flipped a coin and chose French or German. As sexy as it was to have a nation of polyglots, it looked just as confusing. I walked by a group of fair-skinned young men trying to talk to a store clerk. He started in German, to blank stares. They talked amongst themselves in Norwegian, and eventually everyone settled on broken English. Not the most efficient system, but cool nonetheless.

There was no single spot we *had* to see, but we enjoyed strolling the streets, taking in the general feel of the place. Everything was clean, stone, and up-lit. For their sake, I'm glad the Luxembourgers are so rich, or else they'd be grabbing all of their meals from a halal stand like we did. This place was expensive! Nonetheless, we got the last laugh, enjoying the heck out of our kebab in the cobblestone courtyard.

Eventually we'd seen enough and hit the road back to Paris. It was a lovely ride, full of conversation about music, movies, families, and rage against radar speed cameras.

"Hold on guys, do you see that sign?" I pointed out a sign with three lines emanating towards a motorcycle.

"Do you think that means they have WI-FI on the roads??"
I couldn't believe the level of luxury!

"Bro no that's a speed radar you gotta slow down!"

"WI-FI? Really? Tommy be better!"

"Ya that makes more sense. Shoot, Mariannick warned us about this. Keep an eye out with me!"

We fought this battle with big brother the whole trip home, which took us off the beaten path of the freeway in an effort to avoid tolls.

"Tommy you see that? Looks like it's going from one-ten to fifty up there."

"Gotcha, wait it's changing to thirty at the bottom of the hill. Hey why do you guys think that trucks around here have flat faces? They look like goofy pugs or somethi-"

"TEN, Tommy, TEN!"

FLASH!

Another victim of tricky government overreach.

Before I could raise a philippic about the injustice, the limit was back to seventy and the snub nosed truck was honking and flashing its brights at me. I brake checked him like an a-hole and floored it to catch up with the now one-ten limit.

Trying to pretend I wasn't frazzled, I changed the topic.

"So James, your parents are visiting soon, right?"

"Yeah man, they'll be here later next week. I think you guys will like em, they're pretty cool. You know my dad met Mohammed Ali one time? So he was at a bar with his buddies and one of em sees Ali across the place and they start talking and pointing at him, but like then Ali gets up and walks over to their table."

He paused for dramatic effect, Bethany and I leaned in.

"And Ali goes," he raised his hand and slowed down as if quoting verbatim, "I know what you're thinkin, so you'd better keep drinking. I got the key, I'm Mohammed Ali."

"No way, he actually talks like that??" Bethany loved it.

"That's legendary!" So did I.

"Yeah man, when you're on that level you *gotta* talk like that. But then one of my dad's buddies is like, 'Ali, you ain't that tough, whaduya say we go fight outside right now?' And Ali laughs and just says, 'Boy you'd have a better chance with a BB gun in Vietnam!' And walks away just like that!"

We pulled into Stade de Mode a few hours later, surprised to find that a place so foreign could already feel like coming home.

Sunday, February 9, 2020 – Ratatouille

For dinner, we ate the meal I had been waiting for since Pixar planted a seed in 2007 – Ratatouille. Granted, it came from a can, but the stewed vegetables hit the spot.

Back in the room, it was time for some personal grooming. My hairline tells the sad story of a peak and two valleys racing each other to the back of my head. There's not much I can do other than keep it short. I plugged my clippers into an adapter, wondering why the world couldn't agree on a current and prong format. I had to adjust a screw on the side to keep it from taking in too much power and yanking my hair out, but had it dangerously close to the end of its wits. On one fateful stroke, it popped out, the clippers died, and Bethany stepped out of the shower to find a half-naked monk crawling around our tile floor.

"Oh no, what *happened!*" She exclaimed with an amused sympathy.

At a loss for anything clever, I showed her the clippers and looked lost.

"Okay let me help."

"What, like, actually happens if we don't find this. Do I just walk around town looking like Luther before the reformation?"

"You *could* just shave your head."

"That's true, I guess that wouldn't be so bad."

Ten minutes later, Bethany looked in the trash can I had been letting my hair drop into.

"Wait, it's right here! I didn't check earlier because I assumed that would be the first place you'd look, *punk!*" She wagged it in my face.

I grabbed her shirt and pulled her in, putting on my best faux-confrontation face. She held back a smile, pursing her lips and bracing for whatever hoopla might come next.

"You think you're pretty smart huh? You think you're the prized wife of them all, don't you? Well it's true! It's all true and now you're stuck with me!"

Monday, February 10, 2020 – The Game Plan

I don't know if it was the sparse turnout, pouring rain, or desperate need for classroom time, but in lieu of a practice, we stayed in the office installing the game plan. Saturday, we would take on the Molosses.

"Hey qu'est-ce qu'un Molosses?" I asked Jason, one of our running backs.

"What is Molosses? Oh I don't know how to say." He consulted Guillaume in French.

Guillaume was disappointed, "You don't know *any* English, do you? That is easy." He turned to me. "It is 'big dog,' that is Molosses."

"Big dog? No it's not!" Paul interjected.

Jason shot Guillaume a vindicated look. Guillaume flashed him the bird.

"It is bulldog I think. But no worry, we take carry of beezness no?"

"Are they pretty good?"

"Better than the Spartiates, for sure, but not as good as us of course."

Paul said a few things in French to the group, growing impassioned and drawing them in. He turned to James and me.

"I say to them that we are at the very start of a long season, but that we must take one game at a time. Molosses are the next step and we must defeat them before we can go to the next step. This is good, no?"

"Yeah Paul," James assured him, "Tres bon."

James and I were the only two linemen there, and Paul could have our attention whenever he wanted it, so he focused on the wide receivers. Play after play, Paul battled poor WI-FI connection and the team's limited schematic knowledge.

The complexity of high level football would shock most people who haven't been exposed to it. With twenty-two men on the field and numerous situational factors, the strategic options are endless. It takes years of study to know it well. Even now, a real coach has forgotten much more than I know about scheme. Compared to the rest of the room, Paul was operating on a different plane, doing his best to bring the others along.

Most of the receivers wanted to learn, but there was only so much Paul could get across by himself. He was earnest to teach, but seemed comfortable with his limitations, picking his battles and joining in on the occasional distracted conversation. I'm glad; it would be a shame if anyone here didn't enjoy himself.

James snuck an earbud in though his hood and subtly tapped a beat on the table with his pencil. Guillaume passed me a bag of gummy worms that was making its way around the room. Mattias, the backup quarterback, looked up and down from Snapchat most of the night.

I looked through the window at the cold rain pouring outside, cascading by the orange streetlight in sheets. No complaints about a film session tonight. Playing in the elements can be great fun. Anyone who played can tell you about their first game in the rain and rolling in the mud or doing a belly flop in a puddle. If you manage to have fun in the rain, you'll still pay for it the next time to you suit up. Water squishes out of your heavy cleats and the cold shoulder pads make you cringe, stiffening your upper body so you don't feel them move around.

As things wrapped up and I looked forward to chocolate and a movie with Bethany, it occurred to me that everyone else in the room likely had an early morning looming and would rush to bed as soon as they got home. I saw the spotlight pass across the sky and wondered again how I got away with this.

Tuesday, February 11, 2020 – The Kitchen

During college while living with seven other football players, I was *that guy* when it came to dishes. You may laugh but look around wondering if you're the only one who doesn't know which guy I'm talking about. *Is he the guy who never cleans his dishes? Or the tool who designates himself the dish enforcer and won't leave people alone who don't feel like doing their dishes the second they finish them?* I was most assuredly the latter. It seemed like a simple concept and I had very little patience with transgressors. *The problem only compounds the longer you wait!* One time when the dirty stack got out of control, I sent a not-so-passive aggressive text to the house group chat,

"If your dishes are in the sink right now, I hope a non-venomous spider bites you in your sleep tonight."

A moment later one of my roommates sauntered away from his video game and started loading the dishwasher. "That one was surprisingly effective."

Some of my fondest memories lie in that house, but I did look forward to a kitchen where any mess would be of my own doing. That clean kitchen would have to wait. Mariannick warned us, but the women's rugby players were the worst offenders. One in particular had no interest whatsoever in cleaning up. I don't know where she got enough dishes to continue the rotting accumulation.

"At what point do we just clean these for our own sake?" Bethany asked, looking at a freshly ditched pan full of hardening pasta residue.

"We've gotta outlast her, let it get to the point where she *has* to clean it."

"But what if she just *doesn't* care and this goes on forever? We could swallow our pride for the sake of a clean kitchen!"

"Ugh okay. Hold on a minute, you're getting at something from political science."

"Heeere we go."

"No, really! This applies here. It's called Hegemonic Stability Theory"

"Okay, what is it?"

"Well, I'm glad you asked!"

"Make it quick."

"I believe Robert Keohane first derived this idea from game theory, or was it Kindleberger?"

"*Quick!*" She started rinsing the pan.

"Okay! The idea is that collective action will always be a problem, absent a central authority to enforce things. But if you have a hegemon, a most powerful actor, well, that actor might just go ahead and take care of the problem that everyone has, if only out of self-interest. In essence, the problem bothers the hegemon too, but the hegemon has the ability to take care of the problem for its own sake and might do so if no one else does!"

"So what are you saying, that we're some powerful force that will take care of the dishes because it's in our interest too?"

"Well kind of, we're not any more powerful here, but we do have an interest in seeing the kitchen clean and the ability to make it happen. And in international relations, the theory is often used to describe the United States acting unilaterally when no one else will do something. And we *are* the Americans!"

"That sounds controversial, and this is definitely a stretch, but whatever makes you feel better about cleaning the kitchen." She gibed, handing me a plate to dry.

***

Sitting in the office before practice started, Bruno walked past the door in a black Flash windbreaker, and then stepped back.

"Well hello, you had a good time driving around in the weekend?"

"Yeah it was really cool, we drove through Champagne, saw Verdun. And Luxembourg. We even drove through Germany."

"This is good to hear, many times the Americans they come and play video games all day. They talk to me and say 'Bruno I'm so bored!' But there is nothing they want to do." He looked down and adjusted his glasses, seemingly perplexed all over again.

"Don't get me wrong, I play plenty of video games if the WI-FI ever works. My buddies be tellin' me to hop on Fortnite but it won't load. Gets me tight. But I still like seeing stuff. We saw a castle and it was *mad* cool." James added.

"Oh, yes." Bruno wasn't exactly sure what to do with that. "And the car, this was good for the trip?"

"Yeah, no issues other than the expensive gas." I felt bad for complaining after all they were doing to make us comfortable, but sometimes that was the easiest thing to do.

"Well, you know I have a friend, he is inventor. Austrian inventor and I invest with him, he tells me about future of cars. He says everyone in business know that batteries will not last. They are too difficult to refill and recycle. He says they just continue to sell them now, to make the money back they spend in developing. But he invents new electric car that will be powered from magnets on side of the road. You will see this soon. He also makes new full-body umbrella. This will project cameras 360° with live video, so you have invisible cloak." He paused and looked up, thinking through something.

"Ok, have a good practice!" He briskly moved along.

Practice dragged on in the cold wind. At the end, no one was nearby to translate the customary speeches, but I didn't mind. I just assumed Niko was complimenting the offensive line on a remarkable day, telling Sofian what a hoss he'd been. The Molosses didn't stand a chance! We broke it down.

"Yo Tommy my parents just got in if you wanna come say hi real quick!"

I looked and saw two Americans on the sideline bench. Walking up, I noticed his dad sat in a wheelchair but held his head high. His mom had a short haircut, glasses, and must have been the source of his height.

"Tommy! We're so glad to meet you. James told us all about you and Bethany." His mom shook my hand first.

"James what was he going on about after practice? I swear he just kept *talkin*! Tommy good to meet you. You guys looked good first game. Your backup tho? Gimme a break! Did he know he was supposed-ta *stop* the other team? Geez!"

They had some of the thickest New York accents I've ever heard.

"We're awful tired from the flight, so we'll head back to the hotel now, but we'd love to take you and Bethany and your friend Gladis to-"

"*Bad*-is, mom"

"*Bad*-is, to dinner tomorra night, just let us know the place."

Wednesday, February 12, 2020 – Mussels

Just down the road from Stade de Mode, Léon de Bruxelles was the closest thing I'd seen to a casual chain restaurant in France. The Belgian eatery had a green roof, booths, and was well lit, like an Olive Garden with less to spend on interior design. Badis worked a day shift here and was happy to come along as a customer. Bethany and I rode with him, pulling into the parking lot at the same time as James and his parents in their rental car.

Mr. Louison drove, and when they parked, James hopped out and grabbed the wheelchair from the back hatch. He wheeled it around to the driver side door, opening it and gently helping his dad into the chair, making sure his feet were out of the way before pushing forward.

DuoLingo had prepared me for the majestic moment when I would ask for a table in French, but alas this would have to wait. Badis was the man here. As soon as we walked in, his coworkers recognized him, coming up and giving him a hard time for showing up without a uniform. He took it in stride, clearly enjoying being on the other side.

"Now they argue over who gets to serve our table, because everyone knows Americans love to tip." Badis disclosed as we made our way to a long booth.

"So Badis, what's the most popular thing here?" Bethany asked, eager to try something authentic.

"Oh that's easy! *Moules Frites*, that is the signature dish. This is mussels and French fries. Oh they are so *good!*" He closed his eyes, tasting them already. Bethany gave a nervous laugh, never a fan of seafood. The young waitress passed out a stack of English menus. When the moment of truth arrived, Bethany stuck to her guns and asked for some Moules Frites. I opted for a less adventurous fish and chips.

Our food arrived and my mouth watered. Bethany was less amused. A subtle look of panic in her eyes? In front of her was a girthy caldron of steaming mussels, emanating the pungent smell of the sea. She feigned an excited "Alright!" that everyone else seemed to buy.

"So Badis tell us all about yourself, where ya from? How'd ya get here? Brothers, sisters, everything!" Mrs. Louison asked as she got to work on her salad.

"Oh, well, I am from Grenoble in the south of France and come to Paris this year to play with the Flash. I have a younger brother and two sisters." Badis began, maintaining eye contact while he deftly cracked open a mussel, using another shell like chopsticks to pinch out the meat. Bethany nervously tried to imitate Badis. She botched the extraction twice, but scored on the third, slowly raising it to her nose, quickly pulling it back, exhaling, and gulping it down. She beat back a look of horror and nodded along with Badis' story.

"And last year I played for a Division II team in Germany,"

Mr. Louison, who had been keeping quiet and looking around the room, perked up.

"*Germany*, huh? What was that like? Never know what you're gonna get with them I bet. You know we took care-a them *twice*, right?"

"Oh yeah, I had a good time there. The young ones I think are open minded, maybe not in East Germany though."

"What does France think of Germany in general?" I asked, wondering if even one hundred years were enough to move on from what we saw in Verdun.

"Oh it is a good relationship I think. It is like this bully that we now become friends with and work together. In fact I think it's much better than Britain, for example. They are like the old friend who now thinks he is too cool for you and just does his own thing."

Bethany had put down two more mussels, with a bed[8] of them left to go. She caught my eye and mouthed "help!"

I did my best to follow Badis' lead in pulling out the meat. It could use some salt, but wasn't bad. I looked at Bethany and shrugged. *You hate seafood that much?* She looked offended and opened another one with resolve, swallowing it whole and immediately gagging.

The others turned and looked.

"Bethany, honey, how do you like your mussels?" Mrs. Louison asked.

"Umm, they're pretty good! Nice and fresh." She gave a weak smile. Before anyone could ask a follow up, she changed the subject. "So what was James like as a kid?"

"James? I'll tell you what, people always treated him like he was older than he really was because he was big. Tommy, you got that too, right?"

I started to answer but he went on.

"One time he was talking in class and the teacher, this *terrible* teacher, she says to him, 'James, stop talking

---

8 Oh yes, that is their collective noun.

or you *won't get to go home.*' And James is a kid, so he thinks he can *never* go home again! He was *terrified!*"

He paused with wide eyes, giving us a chance to look aghast along with him.

"So James runs outta the room and tries to *escape.* They found him in-a bush by the fence.. but he wouldn't come out! He didn't *trust* any-a them! *Especially* not that terrible teacher!" He exclaimed, hitting the table.

"So what happened then?!" Badis pressed, thoroughly engaged.

"They called me up, and I drove there from my deli as fast as I could! I run up to the bush and told him it was alright, he could come out. While he's huggin me, that terrible teacher comes up to me and she has the *ab-solute* nerve to say to me, I still can't believe she said this, she said, 'Aren't you going to *reprimand* him?" His voice was low and he glared at us.

"I said to her, 'let me tell *you* what. Don't you ever say something like that to *my* son again, or I swear by God I'll sue you and this school for *everything* you're worth."

It was so engaging, I felt like I was in trouble.

The moment we got back to the room, Bethany rushed to our stash of dark chocolate, wolfed down half the bar, and brushed her teeth.

"Ohhh I tried so hard to be polite but that was just *the* worst thing I've ever eaten!"

Thursday, February 13, 2020 – Practice Rage

When the warmup started, James and I were the only two linemen present. While just a week ago I might have been secretly hoping no one else would show for an hour, to avoid leading endless individual drills, I was genuinely excited when my guys started trickling in.

"Bienvenu gran Sofian!"

"Mamadi! Ca va?"

"Brian! What's up man? You had a good day at work?"

Watching the film, I noticed that our double teams were usually impotent. We'd come off hard and make good contact, but someone would run off to the linebacker after two steps, defeating the purpose of the double team. We practiced staying together longer, pushing the tackle back until someone absolutely needed to come off on the linebacker.

"Sofian et Mamadi, en defense s'il vous plait. Washnee tackle et Nyor guard, trente-quatre power." I ran around and gestured at the defense. "Sofian primer, et linebacker Mamadi deux." I ran back behind the line of scrimmage, pointing where Sofian and Mamadi should go at the snap. "A plus! Vert cinq, veeeert-cinq-set-hut!" A mighty clash, eight cleats chopping, and our double team deposited Sofian into Mamadi's lap.

If this was a successful coaching moment, there were certainly plenty of failures. I wouldn't get my point across, the defense didn't give a realistic look, Sofian couldn't run fast enough, a friend would walk by and Moose would leave the drill. But it was unmistakable – we were getting better.

Paul shouted from across the field for us to join the others and Brian called everyone together for our standard breakdown.

"Boo-ya en trois – un, deux, trois,"

"BOO-YA!!" With a pep in our step we darted across the field, like something between a pack of wolves and a herd of elephants.

I have an irrational disdain for the defense that gets downright unhealthy when I'm exhausted. I view defenders as boastful villains, existing only to terrorize my friends in the backfield. Offensive linemen, then, become righteous angels, purveyors of divine justice there to protect the innocent from these fiends and deliver the retribution they deserve. I wouldn't need to be out here fighting if they hadn't shown up as unlawful aggressors, but as it stands, we were all here and I would make them pay. I was the dog, here to protect the sheep from the wolves. Yeah, that's how far it goes in my head sometimes.

Some of the young defensive linemen want to prove themselves against me, and love to talk. Unable to throw their verbal darts directly, they rely on Moose to translate from right guard, who is all too happy to oblige and stoke some good old fashioned controversy.

"Ha! Tommy! He says you are weak and can not stop him!"

"Oh my! This one says you have very small dick and play as if you have injured your p****!"

"Now he says to you, 'F*** Donald Trump!' What you want that I say back to him??"

Well, I've never been any good at talking smack.

"James, handle this one for me."

"Oh brrrrro! You *know* I gotchu." He unloaded a string of mildly creative but wildly explicit insults, to Moose's utter delight.

Forty plays later, the lights went off and we gathered around Niko. *Saturday is the next step in our journey. We need to bring our best and prove our team has returned.* We rushed to the middle with our hands up, until Doukie's encore speech outlasted everyone's deltoid strength. I nodded along until the other hands raised back up.

"Flash en trois! Flash en trois! Un, deux, trois,"

"FLASH!!"

"Un, deux, trois,"

"FLASH!!"

"Un, deux, trois,"

"FLASH! ooOO FLASH!"

***

In August, Bethany started an application for the Army Health Scholarship. It would pay for medical school and give her an exciting repertoire of additional training that would serve her unconventional medical interests well. Despite turning everything in on time, they hadn't gotten her in for a physical before we left the country, and we were in limbo. I walked back into our room to find an exasperated Bethany on her computer.

"Hey. Good news and bad news." She was fixated on the screen.

"Shoot."

"Good news is I don't need to fly back to Chicago for my physical."

"Nice! What could be bad?"

"Well, maybe it's not that bad relatively. Actually yeah it's stupid. I have to go to an Army base in Germany, twice in one week. They said I need to get blood work done one day and then my physical like four days later. And the trains are 'boo-koo'[9] expensive." She added sardonically. "I tried buying a train ticket but the card was declined but somehow still charged us and it was a whole thing but I think we're good now and I cut my hair by myself and I'm worried it sucks!"

"Well, first of all, the hair looks great. Second, I've got two straight bye weekends after Saturday, so I guess we've got another road trip to put on the calendar!"

Friday, February 14, 2020 – Café to Club

Bethany was invited to a get together tonight in the Nineteenth with some ladies from church. After walking

---

9 My fellow Americans, that pronunciation of beaucoup doesn't make us look very cultured!

with Bethany to their apartment, I set off to find a café with WI-FI. We were close to *Parc des Buttes-Chaumont*, a nineteenth-century park high on the north end of the city. I walked down a winding hill, keeping one eye on the sun setting over Paris beneath me, and the other on the storefronts, looking for my perfect café.

Resisting the urge to settle for the McDonalds across the street, I continued on down the hill until I found just what I thought I was looking for. A green and white striped overhang covered outdoor chairs. A smoker and a tea sipper sat under overhead heaters. Inside, a young, fedora trotting barista chatted with two patrons, who may have been students. I walked left into the main seating area and found a table. Looking over my shoulder, I saw two others tapping away at computers, and an older man lost in a book.

The WI-FI network was locked, so I walked over to fedora, standing expectantly in his line of sight. We briefly made eye contact, but he kept chatting away with the favored patrons. Eventually I walked up beside them and asked.

"Excusez-moi, monsieur? Un thé et le WI-FI, s'il vous plait?" [10]

A bothered side-eye before returning to his pressing chitchat.

Did I do something wrong?

"Um, monsieur, excusez-moi?" A bit louder. "Je veux un thé, et le WI-FI?" [11]

He exhaled, raised his eyebrows at his friends, and walked over, crossed his arms and looked at me. I repeated my request one more time. He turned around and had a tea ready not five seconds later, rattling off

---

10 *"Excuse me, sir? A tea and the WI-FI please?"*

11 *"Sir, excuse me? I want a tea and the WI-FI."*

what I can only assume was the WI-FI password while he walked away.

"Merci. Um, monsieur..." *What was the dang word, ah yes!* "répéter le mot de passe s'il vous plait?" [12] He painfully stopped his forward progress, pivoted on a heel back towards me, and rolled his eyes.

"Give it to me." He snorted in flawless English with one partially outstretched hand.

I complied and was connected to the network a second later. As I walked back, I heard him giggling with his minions. So I turned around, grabbed the back of his neck, pinned him to the bar, and spanked him in front of his friends.

Of course this didn't happen, but I was satisfied by the thought, and connected to the internet nonetheless.

I spent the next hour scanning the internet for information on Russia. James Prather booked a flight to visit in May. Ever since he read a pretentious novel, *A Gentleman in Moscow*, we've fantasized about strolling the Red Square in monocles and tweed jackets. This may be our best opportunity.

The sun set and the old man with the book got up and left.

Scanning the budget airline websites, I found flights from Paris for €350. *Oof, pretty steep, but certainly cheaper than Chicago to Moscow. Maybe worth it for a once in a lifetime thing?*

A group of college aged girls strolled in loudly; fedora looked happy to see them. My computer companions started packing up. *Did the music get louder?*

I turned back. A little bit of research told me Russia was charging Americans two-hundred dollars for short-term tourist visas. *Give us a break Vlad.*

Another pack of boisterous hooligans streamed in. The lights were dimming, and the music most definitely

---

12 *"Repeat the password please?"*

191 | GRIDIRON REDEMPTION

got louder. A hazy eyed dude with blond dreadlocks was looking at me, open mouthed. I gave him a polite smile. He bellowed in incoherent laughter.

What kind of quaint Parisian café is this?

When scantily dressed sophomores started dandling up against my bubble of rectitude, it was time to go.

***

Back in Stade de Mode, I noticed James and Badis were in the kitchen, and stopped in while Bethany continued on to the room to take a shower.

"Ça va mon amis?"

"No parler French"

"Sup, Tommy."

I checked the brown bag in the corner for a baguette, grabbed an end piece from the bottom, and sat on a rickety wicker chair.

"Tommy, bro, I was just telling homie about my strength coach from college."

"I can not believe this man!" Badis exclaimed.

"Yeah bro, so we're running this conditioning test, right? And he goes, if Louison can't finish this test in skill time, [13] we're doin down-ups until someone pukes."

"What?? Why you!" Badis was shocked.

"I don't know man! It's like he knew I was one-a the leaders so he wanted to challenge me. Or he's just a psychopath. But anyways, we go and I *haul*, bro. I finish in *less* than the skill time."

"So you do not have to do the up downs, no?!"

---

13 Often timed exercises will account for the radically different sizes found on a football team by breaking it up into three categories. Wide receivers, defensive backs, and running backs, known as "skill," have the least amount of time, while "mid skill," the quarterbacks, linebackers, and tight ends, have a bit more, but not as much as "big skill" or, "bigs," the linemen.

"No, but he comes up to me, gets in my face and he's like, 'I still wanna make you guys do up downs but I'm a man of my word, so I'll let you off this one time."

"I do not understand! He makes the deal, what is wrong?"

"Exaaaaactly bro, it just don't make any sense!"

"I can not believe this, I always think that in America, football is sacred and so all coaches are just perfectly knowledgeable and do the right thing. Like a dream land of football. I never expect there to be a single bad coach."

James and I looked at each other and laughed. I'm flattered he had such a high view of football in America, but really? It was funny thinking of all of the poor decisions and irrational behavior I've seen from coaches during my football career. American coaches are humans too, and *most* of them don't claim to be perfect.

Saturday, February 15, 2020 – Molosses
I checked the Flash WhatsApp group this morning and found a message from Doukie. *Wear your best, team picture one hour before kickoff.* Apparently, we'd be arriving in style.

Thankfully I'd found a gray herringbone blazer at a thrift shop for €10 that fit well enough to wear, even if it didn't a button. I paired this with my dark jeans, the one button down white shirt I packed, and a black tie Badis let me borrow.

My meager effort may have bested James' LIU polo, but it was no match for the rest of the team. When a critical mass finally arrived forty-five minutes before kickoff, you might have mistaken the scene for a GQ photoshoot. Slim fit suits, skinny ties, turtle necks, pocket squares, sunglasses, peacoats, AirPods, and gold chains. The French knew how to dress up. Smoking hasn't

193 | GRIDIRON REDEMPTION

been cool in the U.S. for decades, but somehow Paul and Marcus' cigarettes added to the mystique.

Adrian was quieter than usual before a game. The Molosses d'Asnieres were not only the Flash's top rival, coming from another banlieue just across Saint-Denis, but his former team. I never heard the full story, but remembered him apologizing for some antics last year against the Flash. The Molosses would be a challenge. After beating the Flash last season, they'd gotten off to a hot start, dominating their first game. Their one import, Gabriel Cousineau, was a gunslinging quarterback out of Laval, Canada's premier college football program.

They won the toss and started off fast, making their way past midfield in eight plays and setting up a fourth and eight. The offense stayed on and I watched in horror as Cousineau dropped back, wound up, and aired it out, eying a receiver near the endzone. Not even close. I breathed a sigh of relief. In my experience, when a quarterback lets one fly, he has a good reason for it. If he didn't, he would keep it or throw it out of bounds. I learned to relax when I saw the deep ball today. Every third play was an ill-fated Hail-Mary.

Nyor couldn't make it, so Moose started at right guard next to Washnee. Brian was back at center.

Paul jogged easily up to the huddle, smiled, and delivered the marching orders.

"Spread droit, trente draw. Let's get it!"

On a draw, the line shows pass protection, holding the guise until the defensive line runs upfield, which clears a lane for the running back to sneak by through the middle. Unfortunately, their middle linebacker kept his eye on Guillaume and met him unopposed on the line of scrimmage. Second and ten.

We regrouped and Paul looked less pleased but confident nonetheless.

"Bunch droit, trente-deux zone back." Inside zone right.

Good. Enough of the creative stuff, let's pound it up the middle.

I stepped up to the line to face a behemoth I'd watched on film all week and wasn't sure what to make of. Their three technique[14] was as heavy as any lineman I've ever faced. He walked with a relatively athletic gait, but didn't make many big plays on film. A linebacker walked up in the A gap in front of James, so my job was to singlehandedly push this unit out of the way for Guillaume.

I got low in my stance, picked a target above his right hip, and shifted weight to my left big toe. I was a coil ready to spring.

"Blue dix! Bluuuuuuue-dix-set-hut!!"

I exploded off the line with everything I had, targeting the big man for a punishing blow! Instead, I ran into a wall. Worse, it was a wall that pushed back and I bounced off of him. Guillaume couldn't find space and had to turn right, getting tackled by a rogue linebacker who swam around Moose. Not what we're looking for.

"Combien de taille?"[15] I asked the big man after the play.

Already winded, he responded in breathy French I couldn't understand. Brian heard it and laughed.

"He says one-hundred-and-seventy kilos!"

I looked up for a moment, trying to do the math. *That's like 375 pounds! No wonder.*

On third and ten, Paul found Doukie across the middle but an uncharacteristic drop forced a fourth-

---

14 "Techniques" are used to identify the location where a defensive lineman starts the play. A three technique lines up on the outside half of the guard. Most defenses start with two five techniques (defensive ends on the outside half of the tackle), a three technique, and a 2i (the inside half of the guard).

15 *"How much size?"*

down punt. We didn't say much on the sideline while the Molosses drove sixty-four yards for a touchdown and took the lead. Metanalysis stops when the hitting starts, but a sour turn of luck and time to think can bring it right back.

Maybe we're not actually as good as we think. Maybe there won't be some storybook redemption for the Flash.

It's the first quarter of the second game, shut up!

But look how futile your first drive was and how easy that looked, you're screwed!

The Molosses lined up for the kickoff and sent a squib floundering across the turf. There was a mad dash and a dog pile. Both sides thought they had the ball. The officials were puzzled and after talking it over for a few minutes, admitted they couldn't tell who got it first. Redo play. A similar squib graciously ended up in Flash custody, and that was the first quarter.

"Tommy they are plugging the middle well, I think that we need to run to the outside. Be ready to reach these guys, yeah?"

"Sounds good Paul, let's do it." I replied as we jogged to the huddle near the fifty.

"Ok guys. Trips droit, trente-quatre search, alert opposite. Ready, break."

On outside zone, the tackle needs to set an edge for the running back to get around. The defensive end has to contain the edge at all costs. You can see where the conflict arises.

The play was dialed for the right, but Paul sensed a blitz coming and flipped the play at the line.

"Alert! Alert! Alert! Blue dix, bluuue-dix-set-hut!"

I jumped out of my stance, struck the end in the chest with my right arm, and pushed at an angle, keeping my helmet outside of his. The end had been coached too, and when he sensed what I was doing, fought like mad to get outside of me and push the play back inside. Right when I could feel him start to get across my face, I swung around, pushing him outside towards the sideline as fast as I could with my inside arm. Guillaume was reading my block and took the cue. He cut back inside and powered forward for a nice gain.

We picked up momentum from here; Paul settled into a rhythm, finding receivers while Guillaume powered through holes. Eight plays in, the big man was just as heavy, but markedly less enthused about moving. As long as we ran around him, all was well. Paul fired a seventeen yard laser across the middle that tied the game.

The Molosses trudged on for ten plays, but only managed to gain the same number of yards. They were an offense of extremes. For every fifteen yard gain, there were two incompletions and a ten-yard sack. We took over on our forty.

"Here we go guys, spread droit, X Liza." Paul gave me a nod, he looked excited.

On a screen, the quarterback throws a quick pass to a back or receiver behind the line of scrimmage, who then relies on his offensive linemen to prove their athleticism in the open range, blocking elusive defensive backs. At best, we plow over the menacing little safety twenty-yards downfield while the ball carrier skirts into the endzone. Or, we're juked, proving our athletic ineptitude while nakedly exposed, and leaving everyone to wonder why these fat guys are on the same field as the rest of players. More often than not, it's a sort of awkward in between, wherein we get in their way just long enough to pick up a few yards.

We had two receivers to my left. The inside man would block the corner standing over the outside, who would step back, catch the pass, and run around me, who should be over defender number two. At the snap, the second defender bit a fake in the backfield, and took himself out of the play. When I saw this, I looked down field and saw no one but the strong safety. I changed course and barreled towards him. While I didn't make clean contact, I hit just enough of him that he couldn't reach Doukie, who streaked by down the sideline for a fifty-one yard gain before the free safety pushed him out of bounds. Guillaume jogged in for a nine yard touchdown on the next play, off of a punishing linebacker block by James.

Our defense forced a three-and-out, leaving us time for one more drive before the half. It only took five plays to travel eighty-one yards and put us up 20-6. Half of the gain came on one magisterial pass by the great Paul Durand. Without a roaring crowd, I could hear the *whoosh* of the ball over my head when he launched it downfield to Stefan. No matter that two defenders tailed Stefan by an arm's reach, for IBM's Watson had charted the ball's course. It landed in his hands, perfectly in stride.

"Heck yeah Paul! Nice ball!!" James, Brian, and I smacked his shoulder pads before sprinting downfield to celebrate with Stefan.

In the locker room at halftime, I sat with Brian and Washnee, laughing about the fat man's decrescendo and our feats on the screen. While they continued on, I turned and rubbed my temple. I don't know if it was from the stars I saw running into the fat brick wall, or dehydration and fatigue, but my head was starting to hurt. Anyone still playing football in 2020 has made his peace with the risks of head injuries, but it bothered me nonetheless.

It's probably just dehydration.

I started bemoaning the absence of sports drinks in France, but stopped myself. *I chose to come here, and knew it would be different. This is what I wanted.* I was done with the pitying comparisons.

We picked up right where we left off in the second half, with three scarcely opposed touchdown drives. On the second, we did have to punt, but the kick bounced off of an unsuspecting Molosse, turning it into a live ball that Adrian dove on. We scored three plays later.

On what the clock indicated would be the last drive of the game, the Molosses drove forty-seven yards to the twelve. The game was out of reach, but both sides were battling with everything they had. Pride was on the line between two rivals. If the Molosses were stuck in single digits, that would be a conclusive whooping, somehow different from a more respectable 46-13.

On fourth down, Cousineau dropped back, looking for his slot receiver in the endzone. Adrian read his eyes and jumped the pass, lunging for an interception. What followed was a dazzling display of athleticism, effort, and teamwork as he ran it back ninety-five yards for a touchdown, crisscrossing the field, following blocks and breaking tackles. The entire defense was there to celebrate, swarming their prodigal teammate in unbridled joy. Mimicking an NFL trend, they faced the field together in a tight group, pointing and crossing their arms, posing as a squad for the camera. The camera wasn't there to capture the moment, but they didn't care. Flash win 52-6.

Shaking hands afterwards, one of the officials pulled me aside.

"You make good blocks. Most people in France have not seen blocking like you do, how you use your hands. But I watch NFL and I know what you are doing." He seemed proud, like the two of us were in on a secret the rest of France didn't know. I thought of the Pro Bowl center I briefly played with in Atlanta; he'd probably end up in the Hall of Fame. I was flattered but wished this referee could see the next levels of blocking magic. I'm sure he'd be much less impressed with me.

I finished putting away the orange first down markers and hurried over to Bethany, who was on the sideline taking a picture of James with his parents. *I wonder if this is where they thought the game would lead when they signed him up for youth football so many years ago?* "Oh Tommy you guys played such a good game! We're so proud-a you and James." A beaming Mrs. Louison gave me a hug. "Yeah how bout that, I'll tell ya what I ain't ever seen a three-tech so *fat*. Good thing he didn't have any moves! Course, if he did, he prolly wouldn't be playin here, right?!" He hit the punchline with an open-mouthed smile and raised eyebrows.

Doukie, Brian, Moose, and a number of others came by to greet the Louisons, the esteemed guests of the night. Moose's cordiality contrasted perfectly with his wild dancing in the locker room just minutes later.

Back in Stade de Mode, Bethany and I sat down to what I can conclusively say is the best thing she has cooked to date. The turkey paupiettes were seasoned with thyme and lightly crisped by the olive oil sauté. It was a French recipe she'd found and lovingly prepared.

"My goodness, Bethany! Why does it seem like we're too young to make something this good?"

James and I were conclusively the least fashionable on the team.

CHAPTER V

Bye

Sunday, February 16, 2020 – Pickpockets!

Bethany insisted we stop by a thrift shop on the way back from church. If I could find a leather jacket and blazer for €10 each, she'd be darned if she couldn't find a pair of jeans. While she scoured the racks, I stepped outside to call Chad Hanaoka. Chad and I quickly hit it off at Northwestern, to the point that we roomed together on a bunkbed for three years and he stood as the best man in my wedding. Catching up in the light rain outside of a thrift shop, a middle aged woman stood under the awning next to me and lit a cigarette.

"You're an American too, huh?" She asked, looking up from her lighter.

"Sure thing, how'd you guess?" I heard east coast in her voice.

"You're way too big to be French. Besides, the blond hair isn't from here... and I heard you talkin. You on vacation too? I'm here with my sorority sister for a week, seein' it all."

202 | GRIDIRON REDEMPTION

"No I *live* here, up on the north side." That was more fun to say than explaining the nuance of my eight month stay.

"You live here? Woah, that's another level." She shook her head and took a puff. "I don't think I could do it."

I was simultaneously pleased to feel like an adventurous traveler and curious what she meant, but just then Bethany stormed out. Another failed excursion. I said goodbye to Chad, wished the smoking American happy trails, and walked with my jeanless bride to the metro.

The metro Line One was completely automated, leaving the front of the train open for children to peer through a front window at the track ahead. Children including me, of course. Staring at the rapidly approaching stations, my situational awareness waned, and I didn't notice the three young men slowly moving closer to Bethany and me. It wasn't until a fourth, who clearly wasn't associated with the others, stepped up to Bethany that I knew something was amiss.

"Dee car four" I thought I heard him say, in heavily accented English. Was he asking how to get to Carrefour?

"You'll have to transfer to Line Seven and take the tram towards the hospital. At least that's the closest one I know of."

He looked confused. *Maybe I heard him wrong?* Bethany was wide eyed and stone faced. I gave her an inquisitive look. Just then one of the three others pointed towards the man I assumed needed a grocery store.

"What he say to you?" He demanded from Bethany. She looked at me. I must have been missing something.

"Well he asked where Carrefour was. I told him the closest one I know, which is up off of Line 7, but maybe you guys know another one. I'm sure you do, there seem to be a bunch around here."

They looked confused and then annoyed. The train stopped and Bethany started to get off. Instead of reminding her it was two stops early, I went along with it, wondering what she heard.

"That was weird, why would he ask *us* how to get to Carrefour? Hmm."

"Carrefour? No he didn't.." She looked over her shoulder. "He said 'be careful,' like he was warning me about those guys. I was scared but it seems like you confused them enough that we got off, so I guess good job?"

"Ohhh." That made more sense. I was suddenly grateful for the good man who cared enough to not just mind his own business. Whether he knew that group specifically, or just recognized their behavior, he kept us out of trouble while I was too busy gawking at the children's display.

Soon my gratitude for the fourth man was superseded by anger towards the other three. *Threating Bethany? Are you serious?* For better or worse, any sociological sympathy I feel towards petty criminals evaporates immediately when it gets personal.

Bethany has been an unspeakable blessing in my life. I take seriously my responsibility to protect and care for her; the deep flame I feel when protecting a quarterback, but turned up to a wildfire. I was ashamed that my absent mindedness had put her at risk, even if it could have been worse than pickpockets.

Monday, February 17, 2020 – La Defense

If you've ever Googled a great European city and looked for pictures of the skyline, you may have wondered where the tall buildings are. You notice old monuments and beautiful ten-story buildings, but where are the towering glass skyscrapers that are supposed to define a major city's silhouette? And if they don't have them, how can the cities function without all of that real estate?

Enter La Defense. Directly west of Paris, you'll find answers to all of your questions. Paris had a treasure trove of historic and architectural wonders long before it needed shiny glass towers, but the time did come to need them. Instead of tearing down the old, Paris built the new somewhere else. By and large, bankers, consultants, and multi-national executives don't commute to the Left Bank, they commute to La Defense.

After breakfast and a workout, Bethany and I took the RER west to explore this urban curiosity. We stepped out of the train into a cavernous station, bustling with business suits and briefcases. A series of escalators brought us past coffee shops and grab and go food outlets, and back to the surface. It was the strangest thing. The scene looked like commuter districts in American cities, minus any of the living and cultural space that makes a city, well, a city.

An expansive gray-brick promenade stretched the length of the district, flanked by towering blue and gray skyscrapers, each with its own marginally unique architectural flare. The whole place felt clean and sterile, like it had been designed and built all at once. It was such a stark contrast to Paris proper, as if everything a city needed to compete globally that didn't fit into the Parisian ideal was cordoned off to serve its purpose out of sight. The train station had little choice but to be so large and bustling – there were no signs of cars in sight and everyone was a commuter.

At the center of the spectacle was La Grande Arche de la Défense, an impressive three-hundred and sixty foot tall concrete tesseract. [1] Opting not to pay the €15 admission for a ride to the observation deck, we took in a still stunning view from the bottom. Looking east towards the city, I was amazed by the symmetry. In a perfect line, the La Défense plaza gave way to Avenue Charles de Gaulle, Avenue de la Grande Armée, and finally the Arc de Triomphe.

"I'm gonna go out on a limb here and say they must have planned this."

"Yeah I guess this isn't totally disconnected from the rest of the city after all."

Just when we thought there was nothing left for two non-bankers to do, we stumbled upon an epic Westfield Mall on the south side of the plaza. Escalators crisscrossed four floors with hundreds of stores. The bright lights of movie theatres, clothing boutiques, food courts, kiosks, and everything else under the sun immediately made up for two months away from western consumerism.

We walked into Monoprix, a French superstore akin to Target, where Bethany continued her quest for new jeans. While she set out for the perfect pair, I browsed a rack of T-shirts with an intriguing assortment of American brands. *Harvard, UCLA, New York City, F.R.I.E.N.D.S., Dirty Dancing.*

It wasn't long before Bethany sulked back to me, again in defeat.

"Ugh, I hate shopping for jeans in a place where none of the women have ever done a leg workout. Can we go to Lush? Maybe I can at least find something for my face."

Sometimes I'm bothered when I recognize a company working to get my money. As if I learned their secrets in business school and therefore can't be suckered into falling for the tricks. But Lush deserves the business

---

1 A four dimensional cube. A Google search could be the best option to visualize this one.

they receive, and Bethany had to drag me away from sampling every last bath bomb and brick of colorful soap. Well done, Lush, well done.

As we were gearing up to head back in time for practice, Paul texted me that it was canceled. For the best, I suppose. We now had *two* bye weekends in a row, and I can't imagine the turnout would have been great.

"Hey practice is canceled, so we aren't on the clock anymore." I told Bethany, looking up from my phone.

"Ooo what do you want to do?"

"Well, I did see a Chipotle outside next to the mall..."

"I'm down, I haven't had Mexican food in far too long."

It was nice to occasionally try things from home, like a homesick Swede making his way to Andersonville for some Filmjölk in Chicago. It was nice to have some of the best our hemisphere has to offer. Chipotle doesn't offer the same value in France; we paid €21 for two burritos that may have been two-thirds the size we hoped for, but they tasted just as good.

Tuesday, February 19, 2020 – Flying

I knew practice would be a bit haphazard, and it lived up to expectations. We don't play again for almost three weeks, and Paul is on vacation. Fifteen players were there for the warmup. Despite the low turnout, we had six offensive linemen! I was fired up, seeing our group's commitment. All night, we had the loudest and fastest moving group, having fun and trying new things. During a water break I pulled James aside.

"Hey man, I don't think we're doing any team tonight, hardly any receivers showed up. You got any drills we could do to fill some time?"

He smiled. "Bro, I got just the thing." He spun around and took command.

"Okay guys here's what we're bout to do!" Everyone listened closely, even if half didn't understand. "One guys stands between these two cones and turns around, the other guy runs from five yards back and has to make a move to get around him. Defense can't go outside the cones and can't bull rush. Offense can't turn around until the whistle. Cool? It's mad fun, me and Tommy will show it real quick."

I played defense, charging forward with a swim move after Brian called "hut." James spun around, kept his eyes on my numbers, and pushed me outside the cone. A pretty good rep.

"Okay Mamadi go on D, Sofian you got O. Remember – Sofian don't look until we start, Mamadi don't bull rush."

"Big bull, I hit this now." Mamadi taunted as he bounced out to the five. I wasn't sure what that meant, but hoped he understood the drill. Sofian lumbered to his spot, looking resolute.

"A plus!" Brian yelled. "Blue dix! Bluuue-dix-set-hut!"

Sofian barely had time to spin around and expose his giant chest before Mamadi barreled forward, pounding him with a Zidane style *coup-de-boule*. I started to protest, but the crowd loved it. Moose was prancing over Sofian, who slowly stood up in defeat.

"Not what we were looking for but I love it!" James joined Moose in the fun.

To end practice, we lined up across the goal line for conditioning. The stadium lights went out as we set out across the gridiron. I could see the orange streetlight, small yellow lights in the neighborhood across the street, and the ever-present sweep of the Eifel Tower. My legs and the turf beneath my feet blended into the dark. The wind blew at my back and I felt like I was flying across the cool night sky.

Wednesday, February 19, 2020 – Landstuhl

I'm sitting in a waiting room outside of the eye clinic at the U.S. Army hospital in Landstuhl Germany. You may recall that Bethany has to come here twice, as part of her physical exam. This is the first such visit. Once we cleared the extensive security screenings, we teleported back to the states. Signs in English, American flags, and friendly nods in the hallway. Paris had subtly taught me to avoid eye contact with strangers, so the first two soldiers to smile at me must have found me quite rude, before my Yankee sensibilities returned.

The Landstuhl Army hospital occupies a special place in the American history of my childhood. During the wars in Iraq and Afghanistan, news articles about battles often ended with a note about severely wounded soldiers being airlifted to a level-one trauma center in Germany. This is where they came. Walking the quiet halls, a chill went down my spine as I imagined what tragedy and chaos these walls had seen after the Second Battle of Fallujah or the Battle of Kamdesh. I pictured Bowe Bergdahl hobbling down the stairs, flanked by doctors, psychologists, and curious intelligence officers.

Near the cafeteria, photos on the wall honored each medical service member to receive the congressional Medal of Honor. I did a double take when I noticed an especially long description under a smiling young man with a thin moustache. *Where had I seen that face before? Ah! Hacksaw Ridge!* Desmond Doss had one of the most incredible stories I've ever heard. Motivated by his faith, he saved seventy-five soldiers from certain death behind enemy lines, all without carrying a weapon.

Bethany finished her gauntlet of exams and we left the base with nothing but lunch on our minds. I'm not sure I could have drawn up a better German culinary experience for the occasion. We climbed a wooded hill towards a small old castle one of the soldiers suggested we visit, the view of Landstuhl's quaint red roofs improving with every switchback. It was sunny, a crisp forty-five degrees. I would have learned more about the elegant Nanstein Castle, but the Burgschänke Castle Tavern drew us in.

Either it was a slow day or we'd missed the lunch crowd. The smiling hostess indicated we could sit wherever. The interior was all wood: lighter cedar along the walls and ceiling, darker oak on the floor. Taxidermized boar, deer, foxes, and birds posed above the tables. A full suit of armor stood along the wall. We chose a spot near the window, looking over Ramstein Air Base in the distance, bustling with lumbering gray C-130s. These beasts were the workhorses of the U.S. Military, transporting troops, conducting reconnaissance, air support, search and rescue missions, hauling cargo, and supporting scientific research. The big turboprops did it al-

"Tommy!" Bethany recaptured my attention on behalf of the quiet waitress.

"You know vat you vould like to eat, sir?"

"Oh, yes." This was an easy call. "I'll have the Wildschweinwurst with a bottle of Beck's. Danke."

She feigned a smile, took my menu, and ambled back to the kitchen. A wood burning stove crackled in the corner. I connected to the WI-FI and a slurry of messages flooded in.

"Hey it looks like practice is canceled tomorrow."

"Really? Do you know why?"

I scrolled through the group chat and found the key words. *Le mouvement social.*

"I think more strikes."

"So what do you think? Does this change our plans?"

I bit into the salty vild schvein, thinking about what we could do.

"Well you know, we aren't too far from Switzerland. What do you think?"

"I think I'll find us an Airbnb before you finish that veiner."

***

Bethany's white knuckles clung to the steering wheel.

"Did you see that??" She cried as another Audi rocketed past us. "He had to be going one-fifty, maybe more!"

"Yeah I don't think our trusty Peugeot is winning any races out here." I leaned back. "Let's stay in the right lane." Pedal to the floor and we might have cracked eighty.

The sun was starting to set over the green fields of the German countryside. The small towns were capped by charming but austere protestant steeples. A Porsche tore past us and quickly disappeared into the distance.

There was no speed limit here on the Autobahn.

Less than four hours later, we pulled into Basel and stopped for a walk around. I instantly loved Switzerland. Basel reminded me of a Europeanized Grand Rapids. A mid-sized city on a river with some quiet old streets and a newer center. A stone viaduct bridge cut across the cold water. While Grand Rapids may have a fun history on display in the public museum, it wasn't the gathering point for a crusade, nor did it contend with the bubonic plague.

We had the city mostly to ourselves, save for an occasional street tram or pack of old timers smoking next to a café. I noticed a mix of sophisticated French and alpine German architecture. Protestant churches shared the city with Catholic cathedrals. The cobblestone streets were impeccably clean. Somehow I felt comfortable and safe seeing the white cross on the red Swiss flag.

Walking down one quiet street, a curious sight caught our eyes in the bright lobby of what looked like a bank. A full marching band, dressed in colorful court jester outfits, milled about, casually chatting amongst themselves. Some of them wore hefty masks fixed in maniacal smiles. I looked over at Bethany. She shrugged and we moved along.

Our Airbnb was forty minutes east, further into the countryside. In the dark I could make out a white stucco house with a clay tile roof. As we parked, the front door opened and a short old lady with a knit sweater stepped out to greet us.

"Halo, halo, thank you for coming. Please come inside. I am Herta." An equally short and equally kind old man shuffled in from the kitchen. "Dis is Rudy, we are married fifty years yes. You two are married, yes? I give you two rooms if you are not married."

"Herta, Rudy, it's nice to meet you too. Yes, we're married, only seven months though. I love your house!" Bethany and Herta hit it off.

"Oh you must be very hungry, you travel. Please, leave your bags, come to table." Rudy beckoned us to follow him to a sturdy spruce table. A round loaf of sourdough sat on a cutting board with butter and jam on hand. My mouth watered when I spied a string of sausages and a wheel of cheese.

Herta and Rudy sat with us in their antique kitchen, asking about our trip and sharing marriage advice. Though with less crassness than Pascal, Rudy resorted to pointing one finger up and talking into his iPad when he couldn't find the right words.

"So what did you do for work?" Bethany asked between bites.

"Oh, well, me I was a midwife. Deliver many babies. I never lose one, you know. They say my hands were blessed."

"It is true," Rudy corroborated, "she was the best. People all over town ask her to come. Me? I was professor."

"What did you teach?"

"Oh I teach Latin, Greek, history. Many things. Love to teach, love to learn."

It was getting late and the sausage was gone, so we thanked them for the hospitality and found our rooms upstairs.

Thursday, February 20, 2020 – Fresh Air

We slept until nine and walked down the spiral staircase to find Herta and Rudy busy preparing an elaborate breakfast in the bright conservatory attached to the living room. The Airbnb profile didn't say anything about a complimentary breakfast.

"Oh good morning, good morning. Please come, breakfast is ready. You will have coffee, no?"

"Yes please! Just black is fine." Bethany was thrilled.

"Okay yes, and you sir?"

"No thank you."

"Tea is good?"

"Yes please, green if you have it."

She said something to Rudy in German and he went to the kitchen, preparing the drinks.

"We have new loaf of bread from bakery just this morning. Also we have yogurt, peach and berry, cereal, honey, jam, and good cheese, and more cervelat, oh... sausage, you say. I see you like it very much. Come please, sit down."

Rudy dropped off our drinks, put another log in their wood burning stove, and joined us at the table.

"Very good. You will pray for meal, sir?" Herta looked at me.

"Oh, yes! Thank you. Let's pray. Dear Lord, thank you for safe travels and for our new friends. Thank you for their hospitality and please bless them and their family. You are good and we worship your name. Please bless this food unto our bodies. Amen."

Morning light streamed in, dodging the many plants on its way to our table. The breakfast was genuinely splendid. We learned about their children and careers. They asked about America, France, and how we liked Europe so far.

"We've had a great time, it's a beautiful place and the people have been very kind to us. There have been a lot of strikes in Paris, which makes it hard to get around sometimes." Bethany noted.

Rudy clearly had something to say but couldn't find the words, so he pulled out his iPad. He had a picture of Herta smiling set as his background. Squinting, he raised one finger and spoke a string of Swiss German. The computerized woman piped up a moment later. "The French want to get worked for thirty-five hours straight–" Rudy heard enough to furiously tap the screen, cutting her off. He focused harder and tried again.

"The French want to work for thirty-five hours per week and still get more benefits from the government." He was satisfied with her translation this time around.

"And how about the government here?" The political science student in me couldn't resist. Switzerland was often held up as a model in comparative government classes. "Does it do a good job?"

"Oh yes, government has over seventy-percent support from the people. They do very good job. It is federal system, the model is from American constitution." Herta replied.

As we cleared the dishes, Rudy beckoned me to follow him upstairs. We passed our room on the second floor and continued on to the third, stepping into a small attic bedroom. He walked over to the wall and proudly pointed at a four-foot wood carving of Jesus on the cross.

"Over one-thousand year old!" He exclaimed.

"Wow! That's amazing! Where did you find this?"

"My family has for long time, very long time. Jesus on cross."

We admired it in silence for a minute and then joined Bethany and Herta downstairs.

"So what you will do today?" A smiling Herta asked while drying a plate.

As much as we might have enjoyed a day exploring Basel, we'd seen a lot of historical cities and towns and were craving some nature. Besides, when we pictured Switzerland in the past, it was always alp horns and yodelers in mountain valleys.

"We would love to see the mountains or something else beautiful outside, do you have any recommendations?"

Herta and Rudy were delighted that I asked. Rudy hurried to the cupboards. He came back with a map and spread it out on the table.

On our way out, they hugged us and welcomed us back any time. Everyone vigorously waved goodbye.

The afternoon was perfect. We drove through several idyllic small towns on winding roads, passing the occasional Ferrari, and parked next to an old ski resort at the bottom of a mountain. Apparently there wasn't enough snow anymore to keep the ski business running, but vacationers still came to hike and enjoy the lodge.

A smooth cable car ferried us up the mountain, high over rocky crags and spruce trees before dropping us off on a green hillside just below the snowline. It was sunny and just cold enough to see your breath. The view from here was stunning in and of itself, but a posted hiking map indicated we'd see the alps in the distance if we carried on to the top. They could have filmed The Sound of Music here.

We hiked along a snow packed trail and into the woods, where the ground cleared up. I couldn't hear anything but our footsteps and the wind flowing through the trees. It wasn't long before we made it to the ridgeline and a clear view east. The Alps towered stoically in the distance. Below us - green hills, an occasional farmhouse, and scattered patches of woods. There wasn't much in the long valley between us and the Alps, save for one small town. It was just close enough that we could make out matching roof tops and a church. I wondered who lived there and what their lives were like.

We found a grassy patch in the sun and sat down, gazing at the scene. I put my arm around Bethany and she fell asleep. She looked so beautiful and innocent. I took in the fresh air and thought of John Muir's sanguine words. *Climb the mountains and get their good tidings. Nature's peace will flow into you as sunshine flows into trees. The winds will blow their own freshness into you, and the storms their energy, while cares will drop away from you like the leaves of Autumn.*

***

Saturday, August 24, was an off day for the Atlanta Falcons. We had just lost to Washington 19-7 at home the night before, and were excited for some rest before we got back to it on Sunday. Bethany was in town for the weekend. We were staying at my Uncle Jim and Aunt Jana's house outside of Atlanta, about an hour's drive from Flowery Branch, home of the Falcons facility and my home for the past month. Excited for a chance to explore Atlanta on the off day, we purchased tickets to the Georgia Aquarium.

While I had signed a one year, $495,000 contract with the Falcons, I was making $750 per week after taxes to sweat it out in training camp with a meager chance to make the active roster, where I'd actually make the money people expect of an NFL player. I was on the roster and going to practice, but a long way from being a real NFL player. All that to say, the $84 price tag on two tickets stung, but the reviews promised it would be worth it. My aunt and uncle would drop us off, do some shopping, and pick us up later for dinner in the ballpark district. They had been so hospitable since I signed as a free agent earlier in August and one of the highlights of my time there will always be reconnecting with them.

In the car, however, something went wrong. I got a call from a Flowery Branch number. I knew immediately what it meant, but was either too embarrassed or surprised to answer it. Besides, we were almost to the aquarium and in the middle of a conversation. Maybe I could ignore it until we were done using our non-refundable tickets? Another call, immediately followed by a text, *Tommy, come to coach's office right now. Bring your iPad and playbook.* There is little subtlety in such a text, I had been cut. Again. For whatever reason, I still got out of the car and said goodbye as if nothing was wrong. Finally I called them back. The same thing I read in the text. Why pretend it was anything else? I explained my situation - an hour from Flowery Branch, thirty minutes from my bags, no car.

There was nothing to discuss, I had to get back as soon as possible. Bethany and I looked at each other after I hung up.. and laughed hysterically. Maybe we weren't sure what else to do, or found it ironic somehow. Perhaps we just didn't want to cry about the $84 we spent to not see some incredible fish. But we laughed, hugged, sighed, and finally called my uncle back.

Heyyy, change of plans. I just got fired, could you come back and pick us up so we can get our bags from your house and go talk to my boss for a generous explanation about why I will be on a flight back to Chicago before the sun sets? Sympathetic and understanding, Jim and Jana came back to the aquarium, took us to their house, and said goodbye while we hopped into an Uber bound for Flowery Branch. Coach Quinn and Mr. Dimitroff were indeed generous as they explained their situation. Injuries in the game required some roster moves for another kicker, which meant clearing space on the offensive line, which meant I needed to go. But they wished me the best.

I really did enjoy my time with the Falcons, and it was sad to go. I wouldn't get to say goodbye to the friends I was starting to make on the line. I called a friend in Chicago to see if we could stay in their guest room that night. A scout drove us to Hartsfield-Jackson in a Mercedes-Benz sprinter van, along with another rookie who had met the same fate, and we were off.

Friday, February 21, 2020 – Archaeology

A lot at the edge of Stade de Mode, between a rugby field and the street, has been closed off since we arrived. The high chain link fence keeps intruders away from the bulldozers and front loaders. Something about the construction site just seemed off. There were never more than a handful of people there, and in two months I hadn't noticed anything resembling progress. The workers milled about in blue jumpsuits, focusing on small patches and in no particular hurry. This morning I saw two of them drinking coffee on a bench near our dorm. They looked slender and shaggy, better suited for a library than a muddy construction site.

"Bonjour monsieurs, parlez anglais?"[2]

"Yes, hello. Can I help you?" One of them replied.

"I was just wondering, what are you working on over there?" I pointed towards the mysterious construction site.

"It is a, this is difficult word." He thought for a moment and said it slowly. "arch-e-ology dig, sir."

"Ohh, that is very cool! What are you uncovering?"

He seemed pleasantly surprised by my interest. "Oh, yes! Very cool, yes. We find many things, there was Roman village just here. I am Arnaud, this is my colleague Adrian."

"Tommy, enchanté." I shook hands with both of them.

"You would like to come see? We can give you tour of the dig."

"That would be great! When would work best for you?"

"You come at two o'clock. We show you around!"

"Merci beaucoup! See you then!"

I hurried back to tell Bethany about our new plans for the afternoon. We ate a quick lunch and walked over to the lot. Arnaud saw us and jumped out of the hole he was digging. He brushed his hands off on his jumpsuit and jogged towards us.

"I am glad you come, please come in!" He introduced himself to Bethany, handed out two hardhats, and led us towards the hole he had been working in.

"As I say to you earlier, we find a Roman village, very old. Much to find. Right now, I work on small house, you can see where the door once was, and rooms here and there." He pointed the spots out as we stepped four

---

2 *"Good day sirs, do you speak English?"*

feet down into the partially exposed remains of a stone foundation.

"So how did you know to look here? In this field?" Bethany read my mind.

"In France there is law. Before new construction, there must be survey for historical things. On our survey, we find village, so we have time to uncover all important things before they should build."

Arnaud's jumpsuit displayed the Saint-Denis city logo. I certainly don't remember Grand Rapids having its own archeological department.

"And what are they going to build here?"

"It will be sports center for handicap Olympic games in two-thousand and twenty-four. We become excited when we dig under a sports field because they are well preserved, easy to find many things."

Adrian walked up behind us, eagerly carrying a plastic bin full of artifacts he'd found.

"I find these in house near corner." He let us hold ancient coins, tools, and animal bones. "This is very interesting because we learn some houses come from Gaelic people, before Rome. Then we find that Rome comes to here around three-hundred years before Christ."

"How do you know when the Romans came?" This was awesome.

"We study coins and find emperor on most old coins we find. Also, we know what animals Romans bring, and we can date the bones." Adrian sported a white hardhat with BORN TO DIG [3] emblazoned on the side.

Arnaud led us out of the house and towards a blue tarp that stretched across the whole field. Adrian helped him lift a few rocks off of the tarp and pull it back, exposing an ancient cobblestone road.

3   Ring any bells? It was a play on BORN TO KILL, from Full Metal Jacket.

"This," Arnaud exclaimed, theatrically, pointing towards the conglomeration of rocks, "is our *greatest* discovery: a true Roman road!"

I felt like we should clap, and almost did. Then Adrian chipped in.

"Our hope is that when they will build, they preserve this road. Mybe they cover in glass so people inside can see road below them. We will write a history of the road for people to read."

When the tour was finished, we thanked them profusely and they welcomed us to come back any time to check in on their progress. They handed us each a canvas draw string bag with the Saint-Denis Archeological Department logo, satisfied with their educational efforts and ready to get back to work.

Saturday, February 22, 2020 – Joyeaux and Fanfrale

The forty-person band bounced in sync on the steps of the Opera building. It was a wild scene. An oversized brass section blasted an upbeat refrain while the winds screamed to be heard. Everyone had their own eccentric outfit. Pink tights, blue wigs, overalls, opera masks, tank tops, neon headbands, Hawaiian leis, shutter shades, jedi hoods, skinny ties, cowboy hats, Morphsuits, and anything else you could possibly imagine.

We stood there with several hundred others, nodding to the beat and wondering if anyone else had as many questions as we did. During a decrescendo in the otherwise never ending song, there was a plot twist: the faint sound of an acoustic guitar and a voice, desperate to be heard. I walked a little closer to investigate and found a lone man with his guitar, belting out *Viva la Vida* at the top of his lungs for anyone who would listen. His efforts had cleared a ten foot circle of disinterest in the otherwise occupied crowd.

What was this guy doing? We stayed for fifteen minutes or so and he never backed down. Maybe he was there first and just stubborn. When the brass kicked in he recognized the futility and backed down, strumming his guitar and catching his breath. But as soon as there was a lull, he came back full swing. A few people raised their hands and yelled at him in French, but he was entirely unbothered.

Bethany and I had come into the city to check out Café Joyeux, which was staffed by adults with intellectual disabilities. The cute black and yellow café was packed and full of smiles. We put our bags down at one of the few open tables and I waited in line to order. I asked for a coffee, a tea, and a cookie in my best French. A beaming young lady with down syndrome was thrilled to help, and relayed the order to her colleague, who prepared the drinks, carefully wrapped the cookie in wax paper, and brought it all to me on a tray.

"Bon journée!" [4] She exclaimed with a smile.

"Merci, et toi!" [5]

Once settled, we got to work on our latest project. Bethany signed up for a free trial on Ancestry.com, and we were putting together a family tree. The original goal was to find the names and basic biographical information for every line at least five generations back. We scoured archives and other historical records, slowly piecing together the stories that led to us. I am so fascinated thinking about their lives. Imagine living through World War Two, World War One, The Civil War, or, heck, The Battle of Sempach! Yes, I'm talking about great (15x) grandpa Johan Naef, who lived in Switzerland when the

---

4   *"Have a good day!"*

5   "Thank you, and you too!"

222 | GRIDIRON REDEMPTION

confederation gained autonomy from the Holy Roman Empire in 1386. We got lucky on that one; apparently my grandma Doles shares ancestors with a serious history buff.

Sunday February 23, 2020 – Villanelle

I kissed Bethany goodbye and watched her walk down Platform Twenty-Four, showing the conductor her ticket and stepping onto the Frankfurt bound train. She'd get off in Saarbrücken and switch trains for the short hop to Landstuhl. I stood there until the train left, quietly accelerating and disappearing around a curve. It had been a while since we'd been apart and I missed her immediately. Despite the chaos of pursuing professional football, we were spending much more time together in our first year of marriage than if I had taken a corporate job in Chicago or she'd started medical school right away.

The rest of the morning was mine to wander Gare de l'Est, the Paris East Railway Station. One of the busiest stations in Europe, Gare de l'Est has an interesting history. In 1833, it became the starting point for the infamous *Orient Express* to Istanbul. During World War One, it was where millions of young Parisian men began their, in many cases one-way, journey to the Western Front. Imagine this place packed with green soldiers en route to an uncertain fate in Verdun! This morning, however, was peaceful. Birds chirped in the rafters, tourists and businessmen milled about, waiting to board. I found a table in the station's Starbucks and sat down for some reading and writing. American pop Christmas music, peculiarly, hummed throughout the station.

I checked my email and looked sadly at a rental application. We had to start thinking about our upcoming move to Tennessee, and while we once had dreams of buying a house or even a duplex, it seemed too difficult and we'd settled on renting. Maybe after medical school. Bethany had found a nice apartment that wasn't as cheap as we hoped for in the area, but looked nice enough. I closed the email and opted to fill it out later.

I'm going to write the third installment of my annual Valentine's Day poem for Bethany, albeit a bit late. The first year, I had the audacity to write my then-girlfriend a Shakespearean sonnet. Year two, my fiancé received an old fashioned acrostic. If all went according to plan, my wife would have a villanelle in her inbox before she crossed the border.

The five tercets and single quatrain proved more difficult than originally expected. I was intrigued by Dylan Thomas's well-known poem "Do not go gentle into that good night." After two hours of willing out creativity, I had a serviceable collection of rhymes, and sent it on to my bride who deserved much more than that.

Monday, February 24, 2020 – Fortune 15

"Une, deux, trois,"
"BOOYA!"

James, Mamadi, and I broke it down and jogged to Niko and the others at the fifty. We were the only linemen tonight and tried to make the most of the short practice. After two three-hundred yard gassers, we were out. Walking out of the locker room, I checked the time.

"Hey James, it's 10:30, do you mind if I take it now?"

"Sure bro here ya go, good luck." He unplugged his white earbuds and handed me his iPhone 6.

"Thanks man, I really appreciate it. His assistant said he'd call sometime after 10:30. I'll get it back to you ASAP."

I had a call to take from the United States, but the only phone plan to my name was in Bethany's pocket, en route to Paris from Landstuhl. James had been kind enough to lend me his. For someone who utilized the screen as often as he did, this was quite generous.

Eleven o'clock came and went. I sat at my desk now, notebook open, tapping a pencil. Watching James' phone buzz with every imaginable notification except the one I was interested in. Bethany arrived in Gare de l'Est and was on the metro back towards Bobigny. At 11:30, it rang with an American number.

He was the CEO of a fortune 500 corporation who had crossed paths with my dad earlier in his career. He was a former football player himself, and had loosely kept up with my career. When he and my dad saw each other around Christmas, he offered to talk to me about my next steps. I'd gotten in touch with his assistant and set this up weeks ago.

I learned about his career and moving on from football. From the early days as an entry-level salesman to the stratosphere of corporate power, football had stuck with him. Offensive linemen in particular, were intelligent, hard-working, selfless, and loyal. He talked to me about discovering what I wanted to do and finding the right job. He even invited me to their headquarters to shadow him and any other executives I wanted to. We'd reconnect when I got back stateside.

Around midnight, I thanked him for his time. He was happy to do it - someone did it for him when he was my age. Besides, he respected the heck out of my dad.

We hung up and I leaned back in my chair, sighing and rubbing my eyes. *Why was I as stressed as I was excited?* For one, it was a stark reminder that this victory lap abroad wouldn't last forever. That I would need to move on, and soon. But there was something else. We were talking as if my issue was figuring out what I wanted to do in the business world, but while I had every opportunity to fall in love with corporate America at Northwestern, there was an entirely different realm of possibilities that I couldn't stop thinking about.

Politics, diplomacy, security, development, academia, ministry, or some combination of this ambiguous but fascinating world. On top of that, I had chosen, with my eyes wide open, to get married to a woman set on medical school, committing to support her in that dream. She deferred starting for a year to follow me wherever football might take us, but would start classes in Tennessee in August. Sitting in our little room now, I felt the weight of the future bearing down on me. I knew my time was coming to hang up the cleats and move on. It just felt closer than ever. Like it was in the room with me. *Who am I without the game? What now?* Beyond that, I somehow had enough potential that this CEO wanted to talk to me. What if I didn't live up to it?

I knew that as a Christian, my value and identity came from God, and no circumstance could change that. But that was easy to talk about when I played in front of roaring crowds on national television. When people tweeted about me and asked for interviews. Without the fanfare, I had to practice what I'd been preaching about contentment in Christ alone.

I thought of the Flash. No one really cared about them or told them how great they were. Fans didn't recognize them in restaurants or ask for autographs. But somehow, they were content. The relationships and the process were enough of a reward to keep them coming back for more.

Bethany walked into the dorm as I was thanking James profusely. I'm more confident in my love for Bethany than in anything I want to do professionally. We'll be fine. The cares drifted away for the night as Bethany told me about her time in Landstuhl and we fell asleep watching The Sound of Music.

Tuesday, February 26, 2020 – Roughriders

I sat down by our desk after a quick workout at Fitness Park and saw a text from Bob Engler. A CFL team, the Saskatchewan Roughriders, wanted me to play for them this season. Not a tryout, but a guaranteed roster spot. Training camp starts in May.

If an American knows anything about football in Europe, chances are it's because they read *Playing for Pizza*, a delightful novel by one of America's great storytellers. Quarterback Rick Dockery flees the NFL for Italy and plays a season with the Parma Panthers. Once the Browns third string quarterback, injuries forced Rick into the AFC championship game, which he blew in spectacular fashion. Italy was his last resort. At one point, his agent calls, telling him he had a spot in the CFL. The team had even booked a flight to Toronto, no strings attached. Rick reluctantly took the trip, only to find out in the airport that the coach was also courting another quarterback. He abandoned the trip and flew back to Parma, with a quick stop in Cleveland to punch his biggest press critic in the face.

There was no such drama in my situation, but I felt some melodramatic solidarity with this fictional fellow NFL reject. Like him, I found a new home, a family that embraced me. I could never abandon them the middle of the season; someone had to protect Paul's blindside. Besides, we've got things to do and places to see. It was an easy call.

Thanks Bob, but please tell them I'm not interested, I'm happy over here. Hope you and the family are doing well.

Wednesday, February 26, 2020 – Real Estate

The inclement weather was confusing, transfiguring from hail and dark clouds to a clear blue sky and back in twenty-minute cycles. It was enough to keep us in our room most of the day. Our Ancestry trial ends tomorrow, so we worked on filling in details on my spreadsheet.

Even though we'd mostly resigned to our fate of renting in Tennessee, I reached out to two trusted people to hear their thoughts on buying. My Uncle David was a business owner and real estate investor who has always been savvy with money. Nick Castelluccio, the director of Athletes in Action Chicago who married Bethany and me, owns and lives in a triplex and can offer grade A advice about pretty much anything. My main question – are we doomed to renting an overpriced apartment, or could we pull this off? I was surprised to hear their responses.

Overall, my suspicion is you could make money and come out ahead with the real estate option, but it would increase risk and take more time, work and effort.

Personally, I wouldn't hesitate in purchasing a home there. Interest rates are so low right now, you'll spank 3% in the market. As far as getting a loan, worst case scenario you get a cosigner. The stakes are relatively low and the opportunity to learn and build equity are great!

Hold that rental application.

Thursday, February 27, 2020 – Soccer Skills

At eight o'clock, fifteen of us stood together, watching a youth soccer practice wrap up. They were on the field and we couldn't do much but wait for them to get off. A ball rolled over to a group of defensive linemen. When the ball settled in front of Yuwan, our tall musclebound defensive tackle, I expected him to kick it back and carry on his conversation with Gigi. Instead, he casually flipped the ball up and started juggling, bouncing it between his knees and cleats. When he had enough, he kicked it over to Charles, who did the same. The ball bounced around the circle, never hitting the ground while they casually continued their conversation.

Brian noticed James and me gawking at the scene.

"What's wrong guys, you haven't seen juggling like this before?"

"Bro, I've seen it before, but like, not from *football* players!"

"Yeah how come they know how to do that? I figured the guys who play football in France were the guys who were too big or just not good enough at soccer!"

"Everyone knows how to play soccer here, we do it since we were young!" He shook his head and laughed. "Sometimes I forget America is the only country that just doesn't mess with soccer, even though you good at everything else."

He called to the D-linemen in French and they laughed, kicking the ball towards us.

"Let's see what you got!"

I bounced it awkwardly on my knee a couple of times. James stumbled and nearly fell.

After practice, we sat in the car with Badis, heading back to Stade de Mode when we noticed no small commotion at the *8 Mai 1945* roundabout. Police vans crowded the area and a crowd stood around the tram platform. The traffic didn't stop, however, so we kept moving. At home in the hallway, Sotiris was pacing in front of his room, looking distressed.

"Yo Soterees, bro, what's up?" James asked, slinging his bag to the other shoulder.

"Um, I don't know how to say, but I see *terrible* thing."

"Was it something by the Metro stop?"

"Yes! You see this too?"

"We just saw the police cars, what happened?"

"Well, I get off of tram, I was in Paris shopping, and I hear loud cry and see a man run away. Then I look down and see the guy with knife in his neck and blood comes out, very fast. We stand in circle around him but not know what to do and very fast he stop his moving. Ambulance comes in two minutes but that was too late."

He winced, reliving the painful memory.

"Oh no!" Badis was stunned. "Do you know who it was or what happened?"

"No, but I think that it may be one of the, I don't know how to say..." He gestured like he was handing things out. "Moboro moboro, cigaro cigaro. Those guys. Maybe they are rivals."

"It must be that." Badis posited. "And very likely they are undocumented immigrant. Probably nothing will happen."

The numbers tell me La Courneuve is far safer than Chicago, but it's chilling to think about this happening so close.

Friday, February 28, 2020 – Frog XVI

A quick Google search this morning turned up an official response to the stabbing incident from the local authorities. Violence related to illegal cigarette trafficking. They knew about the problem and have been trying to tell the Minister of the Interior they needed more police officers, but he wouldn't listen. They told him again and hoped he'd listen this time. Apparently cyclical blame games happens everywhere.

Blake and Mary arrived in Paris this morning, checking into their hotel and recuperating from the jet lag. Blake was enjoying the free time of an NFL offseason and Mary had taken a week off from her job in consulting. We hardly feel qualified to show anyone around Paris, but are happy to give it a shot.

I asked a friend from church what to do on a rainy night in Paris if you can't afford to see a show or eat at a Michelin star restaurant. He told me to find a nice café and sit there for four hours. Sounds good!

The café we found on Yelp turned out to be closed, but Bethany saved us from kicking off the weekend as inept hosts by finding a casual brewery not far from the rendezvous point. It wasn't difficult to spot them walking towards us in the light rain from two blocks away. Blake stood a head taller than the surrounding Frenchmen and sported muscles inflated far beyond Parisian norms. Bethany and I were so isolated in Paris that it felt like we moved to a different dimension. Seeing Blake and Mary, I couldn't decide if they'd joined our new universe, or if Paris really was in the same world we left two months before.

Frog XVI was just the sort of place we might have picked for a meetup in River North, and we spent our time in just the same way: catching up, reliving old memories, and talking about the future. Last month when I briefly told Blake about the Barcelona debacle, he promised to pay for the first dinner if we stuck around. True to his word, he slid a card across the table to the waitress and we were off.

It was a short walk from Frog XVI to the Eifel Tower, and we agreed to make the trip before calling it a night. Turning the corner onto the Place du Trocadero, we stopped in our tracks, taking in a dazzling view of the tower, glittering in its hourly show. I don't know how long it takes for the locals to grow numb to the view, but I certainly wasn't there yet.

Saturday, February 29, 2020 – Missing Out

Happy birthday Jimmy! It was younger brother's fourth birthday today. Fourth *real* birthday, that is. Born on leap day in 2004, he typically settled for a counterfeit on February 28. He was having friends over for Pizza and a game night. I was sad, thinking about another beautiful moment at home I would miss because I was off chasing a football dream. There's an opportunity cost to adventure, and since I left for Northwestern, that cost has been counted most acutely in weddings, birthday parties, cookouts, and other such get togethers in West Michigan.

The example that weighs on me the most was missing my Grandpa's funeral. I came home as soon as I finished my last winter exam in 2015 and went straight to their house from the train station, only to find that he had succumbed to ALS less than an hour before. I spent three special days with my family, but had a flight to catch to a mission trip in East Asia, putting me in the air on the day of his funeral. Spending the week serving, learning, and sharing the Gospel felt like time well spent, but the cost was still there!

***

I threw on my brown leather jacket from the thrift shop and ran out of the kitchen, careful to dodge the latest pile of crap on the sidewalk. Blake and Mary would meet me at the end of Line Seven, *8 Mai 1945*. I guessed which escalator they'd arrive from, leaning against the wall with one foot kicked back behind me. The picture of confident wanderlust. After a minute or two, I second guessed myself, walking towards a different escalator, dodging commuters and looking around.

"Hey! Can I help you sir? You look lost." Blake grinned as they walked up behind me.

"I guess I'm still finding my way around. Welcome to La Courneuve."

At the top of the platform, they immediately looked at the circle of flowers around a pile of sawdust.

"Umm, what happened here?" Mary had her suspicions.

"Uh yeah someone got stabbed in the neck two nights ago." I grimaced, then gestured to the rest of the bustling roundabout. "But it's a nice place!"

I led them to Stade de Mode, pointing out the landmarks that tourists never come to see, but were pivotal to our experience.

"That's Fitness Park, where we work out. Then to your left is Carrefour, the supermarket, they've got a great bakery too. Now on your right that's the hospital where Bethany shadows sometimes. This is where we get off."

Making the most of our shared kitchen space, we set the table with our best plates and cloth napkins. I'd run to the boulangerie earlier for croissants and a pan au chocolat. Our egg scrambles were starting to get out of hand, they were so good. Smoked sausage, rich eggs, generous sprinklings of salt and paprika, two French cheeses, and diced peppers. After brunch, we gave them the grand tour of our room and headed to the train for a day in the city. Much as we would have liked to introduce them to our new friends, Badis was at work, James asleep, and the rest of the Flash out of the office for the weekend.

Walking to the tram, the sky opened up for just a few minutes and we were apocalyptically dumped on. Standing under the platform's awning, precipitation violated us from all directions, incessant rain permeating our clothes and backpacks while hail stung like a swarm of bees. As quickly as it started, the menacing cloud moved on, leaving a blue sky and gentle breeze. Blake looked around, wiping his face off, equal parts confused and offended.

"What the *hell*?!"

We spent the afternoon strolling Montmartre, exploring the neighborhood and Sacré-Cœur. For dinner, we decided it would be adventurous to set out in a new direction and walk until we found something that looked good. The idea was charming at first. Along a tall stone wall, a young couple eagerly made out. I was about to make an obligatory comment about the city of love, when someone in an ornate chicken costume walked up to the lovers and starting twerking, much closer than the average couple would appreciate. I braced for a fight, but moments later the three twerked together, all smiles. Whirling around to see if I was the only one so befuddled, a camera crew politely indicated we were in their shot.

Scarred from this morning, we all got anxious when drops of rain began falling on our still-wet clothes. Mary saved the evening by spotting a hole in the wall café not far from Moulin Rouge. Inside, the man behind the bar raised his eyebrows and looked towards us. I was ready to show off.

"Bonsoir monsieur, une table pour quatre s'il vous plaît?" [6]

Giving me far too much credit, he replied with a rapid bite of slurred French. Blake, Mary, and Bethany looked at me expectantly. *Well shoot, they say you're only one question away from exposing yourself as an idiot.* I used some deduction and two words I thought I'd heard to reply. *Let's see, 'manger' to eat, 'boire' to drink, right?*

"A manger, s'il vous plait."

He grabbed four menus and indicated for us to follow him. I smiled, far too proud of myself. Bethany could tell and rolled her eyes.

---

6 "Good evening, sir, a table for four please."

The restaurant had a low ceiling, bricks walls with impressionist paintings, and yellow tables. Millennials as we are, we briefly considered ordering snails for the sake of an "authentic" experience, but thought better and found other sufficiently French dishes. I ordered a duck breast and Bethany goat cheese with ham. If I've had duck before, it was a long time ago, and I couldn't believe how beefy the meat tasted. Given the size of the creature, I assumed it would taste like chicken.

We ordered crème brûlées and a bottle of red wine.

"Guys," I started, holding my glass up slightly. "When we were all together in San Diego, I remember looking out at the harbor and being struck by something." Bethany crossed her arms, suspecting where this one was going. She knew all of my jokes.

"And I couldn't help but think to myself. There are all kinds of ships. Big ships, small ships, cruise ships, cargo ships, military ships. But! The *best* ships?"

Bethany reluctantly raised her glass and mouthed the punchline with me.

"Are friendships!"

Everyone joined the toast, good sports as they were. Blake and Bethany laughed and rolled their eyes, Mary smiled politely. We called it a night.

Sunday, March 1, 2020 – Deep Woods

While we waited in line to renew our metro passes, a middle-aged woman with a child cut the entire line, marching to the front and getting to work on the kiosk. I looked around. *Who does she think she is? Did anyone else see that?* Crickets. Perhaps she was an old money aristocrat, the countess of Bordeaux. Or there was an admirable deference to women with children. Chivalry may not be dead after all.

Bethany and I went to church, but left before the mall hangout, opting for an extra couple of hours with Blake and Mary, which we spent exploring the Pantheon, the final resting place for great men and women from France's history. We stopped for macarons on our way to the lovely Jardin des Tuileries, a beautiful symmetrical garden on the river. A straight line connects the Louvre's pyramid, the main path in the garden, the center of the garden gate, the obelisk in Place de Concorde, Champs-Elysées, and the Arc de Triomphe, which of course continues another straight line on to Arc de La Defense. I'm looking forward to spring afternoons strolling the gardens and reading a book on one of the benches. The sun was low in the sky when we reached Place de Concorde. Everything was golden and glistened in the aftermath of rain.

***

If there were a big forest, how deep could you possibly go before you're no longer heading into the woods but out? At that point, what would it be like? Would it be the purest, most concentrated form of the woods? With as little contamination from the outside as possible?

I've thought about authenticity like this. How close can we get to the *itness* of a people or place before we start moving towards something else? When I was younger, I'd spin the globe in my parents' office, searching for remote cities that were *deep in the woods*. When I found an intriguing one, I'd google it and scroll through pictures, wondering what it would be like there. A city in the middle of the Sahara Dessert. The most remote island in the Pacific. The airport furthest into the Amazon. Heck, I still do this. But it isn't just the remote and the extreme. Even a town conclusively on the grid has a soul to be discovered. Maybe it's a famous landmark, but more often it's a hole in the wall restaurant two blocks from Moulin Rouge, or a living room in Souilly.

But *why* search deeper in the woods? Why hunt for authenticity? New experiences are usually good. The new stimuli are exciting and help us grow. In an increasingly connected world, the cosmopolitan centers start to look the same. Finding something new and unique? That's hard. But when you do, there's wonder. Something to learn. From a Christian worldview, diversity gives us a fuller view of who God is, since *all* of mankind is made in His image.

If none of this was articulated, it was on our minds when it was time to pick a place for dinner. We walked around and nothing stood out until we came upon a small Thai restaurant in The Second.

"Guys this looks good."

"But Thai food? Shouldn't we have something Parisian?"

We thought about it for a second.

"Well, hear me out." I started. "Paris is multicultural. Yesterday, we had a classic hole in the wall Parisian dinner. Tonight, we could experience the modern side of the city. Besides, we haven't had any kind of Asian food since we got here." The justification was mostly for myself.

We sat down in a black leather booth with a wooden lamp and stained bamboo shoots along the walls. Any doubt this was the right place for tonight dissolved when the waiter placed a plate of Pad Thai in front of me. The others looked similarly pleased and we dug in. We stayed for two hours, enjoying the food, the ambiance, and mostly the company. The conversation went all over the place, but always felt engrossing.

Blake and Mary were planning on flying to Rome tomorrow morning and spending the week in Italy, but I'd seen some worrying news lately.

"I'm sure you guys are following this, but did you see there are some more cases of the virus in Italy? Think that will impact your plans at all?"

"We're still planning on going and everything, seems like it's mostly in the Northern part of the country," Blake replied.

"But then again who knows, we never thought it would get out of Wuhan. Maybe our flights will get canceled and we'll be stuck in Rome," Mary added, taking a sip of her wine.

"I guess I can think of worse places to get stuck!" I made light of it, but what started as a very distant problem was getting hard to ignore. Could it come to France next? America?

"Bethany you're a doctor, why are we making such a big deal out of this when the flu kills way more people every year?"

"Well first of all, you of all people know how far I am from being a doctor, but I think there are a few things. For one, since it's a novel virus, no one in the world is already immune to it and there's just so much we don't know, which freaks people out. And then it looks like this is something like ten times deadlier than the flu, so if we can stop it from becoming an annual thing, that would be great. If we could just get rid of influenza, we would, but it's too late for that now."

"I guess that makes sense. I just remember Swine Flu and Bird Flu coming around when we were kids. People made such a big deal of it at first, and then nothing really happened."

"Well, let's hope that's the case this time too." Blake concluded.

We paid the bill and parted ways with hugs and promises to stay in touch. While they walked towards their hotel, Bethany looked at me.

"They're so great, I want to stay friends with them."

"Ha, I agree. Me too. It's sad thinking we won't be around them and other college friends like we used to, but nice that we can always pick up where we left off."

"Yeah, and also that as much fun as dinner was, we didn't need to be in Paris for it."

"I guess it's more about the people than we usually think."

A peaceful Alpine moment that I never wanted to end.

Bruno doesn't trust Americans with a stick, but this Peugot got us around.

CHAPTER VI

Vikings

Monday, March 2, 2020 – Big Man?

I stood in line in Carrefour, grabbing a few things on my way back from an upper body workout at Fitness Park. A short old man with a big grin shuffled behind me in line, bellowing into his cell phone. He hung up and said a few things to himself while he put the phone away. When he looked back up, he saw me and started laughing. I turned towards him, offering a confused smile.

"Umm, bonjour monsieur?"

"Russo! Russo! Ha-ha!" He pointed at my head and spread his arms apart.

"Russo, monsieur? No, I'm an American."

"Big Russo! Vive Putin! Ha!"

"No, *AMERICA*. I'm American. *USA*."

"Russo box!" He stuck up his fists. "Russo box, break you. I must break you! You say! Ha-ha-ha!"

I can't say it's the first time I've heard that one. My new friend kept laughing to himself while I checked out and left. On my way out, I heard a new one sided conversation forming with the cashier.

This weekend would be our first road game, a matchup against the Vikings in Wattignies, a small town near the Belgian border. The Vikings had recently moved up from Division II, but at first glance, didn't appear to be much of a threat. They ran an odd defense, meaning three down defensive linemen instead of the usual four. I always hated playing against odd fronts. One less defensive lineman meant one more linebacker who could come from anywhere. Everything seemed more complicated and fast moving. It was harder to fit double teams. Based on the few clips we watched, however, the Vikings don't run the defense with the same wrath as Wisconsin.

Standing under the bleachers after practice, waiting for Paul to come in with the key to the locker room, I found a scale in the storage closet and weighed myself. 114 kilos. That can't possibly be right, can it? Certainly, it must not be! Several others tried and confirmed it was spot on. That's 251 pounds! At one point with the Bears, I tipped the scale at 308. During the fall, I dropped down to 270, but found my way back to 280 at home for Christmas, thanks to the legendary Doles kitchen. I arrived in France around 275. When did I lose all of this weight?! I've always struggled to gain weight and now being away from the endless food of a Division I or NFL team, it feels almost impossible. My clothes are starting to fit differently, and the ring I could barely get over my finger at the alter is threatening to fall off.

There's something more to be said about offensive linemen losing their weight. Very few elite linemen grow up morbidly obese, but rather lean and athletic. Putting on weight is a job they take on in high school, and with vigor in college. Many of us look forward to eventually losing this weight. It's hard to do this to your body! When I was journeying from a 6'4 185lb high school freshman to a 6'4 308lb NFL hopeful, I ate four big meals per day, lifted heavy four times per week, and never went bed without a full stomach. While I won't pretend I didn't enjoy it, eating became a job. But it was more than a job, it was an identity. You don't "play offensive line" you *are* an offensive lineman. You're big! You eat big, lift big, and look big. Your clothes are big and don't fit well, people slide their leftovers to your end of the table. You occasionally break chairs. We embrace it, but we all know this isn't something you do forever. You won't live very long doing that. Already your joints and back rebel against the onslaught of gravity. So when the time comes to hang up the cleats, it begins an ensuing transformation. You may not recognize a lineman six months after he retires. Time and again, retired linemen shed exorbitant amounts of weight, sometimes one hundred pounds in a year.

But I am seeing that this has a hidden cost, indicative of larger struggles that come with retiring from a sport you love. You aren't just shedding weight, you're shedding your identity as a lineman. You can't really be *one of the guys* anymore if you don't have a forty-six inch waistline. People won't recognize you in public as a football player because of your size. I had always envisioned a clean break from my time as a lineman to my time as a NARP. [1] But now I'm in an awkward in between. Not big enough to be a true big guy but holding on to what I've got left. Raging against the dying of the big.

---

1 An uncharitable acronym used by college athletes to describe non-athletes: Non Athletic Regular Person.

Tuesday, March 3, 2020 – Vivaldi

Every year, the Northwestern community reads a book together. At least that's the idea; shamefully few students actually participate. My freshman year, we read *Whistling Vivaldi*, by Claude Steele. The book explained the Stereotype Threat, where individuals feel pressure due to awareness of a stereotype about their group. Tests showed that Black men scored significantly lower in a game of mini-golf when they were told beforehand that Black men typically scored lower than the rest of the population. Absent this awareness, their scores were in line with the rest of the population.

Steele shares his experiences with stereotypes, noting that he could put passersby at ease if he whistled Vivaldi tunes while he walked down the street at night. It framed their mind to a different, safer, stereotype – a classical music aficionado, rather than whatever negative stereotypes they carried towards a Black man. While I don't know what life would be like as a Black man, I am occasionally aware of how I, a rather large man, make others feel.

Walking back to my house in Evanston one night, I saw a young woman ahead whom I'd inevitably be passing on the sidewalk. Thinking back to *Whistling Vivaldi*, I figured I'd give it a shot as a gesture of goodwill. The problem was, I'm an atrocious whistler. So when I tried to whistle the famous line from Vivaldi's *Spring*, I sent out an ominous ghostly crackle. She crossed the street and sped away. You hate to see it.

In La Courneuve, I find myself subconsciously embracing anything intimidating about my appearance as a defense mechanism against the unknowns of a new place. Especially on the tram at night with Bethany, where I want to look as big and tough as possible. But last night, I was walking past an older lady with groceries. On a dim sidewalk, she might have been frightened by a large man walking towards her. I considered whistling *Spring*, but thought better of it and gave her a smile instead.

***

Paul lined up, hands under the center, and called out the cadence.

"Blue dix! Bluuuue-dix-set-hut!"

Moose's snap was off to the side, and by the time Paul got control and stepped back, James was pulling out of his stance at breakneck speed, eyes set on the defensive end. An offense runs like a clock. Finely tuned parts working together. When one part is just slightly off, things quickly cascade downhill. James' heavy size fourteen cleat landed squarely on Paul's much smaller left foot.

"YOOOOWWWWOOOOO!!" Paul cried, bouncing around on his right foot. Everyone stopped. James and Moose both turned around in horror. Niko called for a water break and Mattias started warming up. Paul was sitting on the bench with his head down, painfully trying to pull off his cleat. I looked over and saw Mattias throw a duck to Doukie. I could think of few things worse for our team than losing Paul. That and this virus finding a way to interrupt the season. I heard that the government, worried by what they saw in Italy, was considering limiting public gatherings to five-thousand people. Fortunately, the Flash crowds weren't a threat.

I'd seen plenty of things in our practices that looked like injuries waiting to happen. Tackling to the ground, no whistle to stop one-on-one reps, fifty full contact plays two days before the game. But a botched snap leading to a crushed toe? That could have happened anywhere. It was just unfortunate.

246 | GRIDIRON REDEMPTION

We finished out practice with Mattias at the helm. He knows enough to manage the offense and I'm confident we'll have the firepower to sink the Vikings, but I hope Paul isn't out too long. After practice, Niko talked for a solid ten minutes. When the players start switching the knee they have down, it should be a sign the coach has been talking too long. Brian got less motivated with his translations as it went along.

"He is pissed off concerning the special teams. He says they are dumb and don't know where to go. Left is left, right is right. He says we have to have better practices. Just because the Vikings are not good does not mean we can have bad practices. Now he is pissed off concerning the defense. I don't know how to say this in English. Never mind this now. He says for the Americans to stop touching yourselves so much."

I perked up.

"I'm just kidding bro, I make that up. Okay he says to have a good night and go home now."

We raised our hands together and Doukie began his second act, passionately exhorting the team to do something. The tired arms slowly went down, and then back up for the real breakdown.

Wednesday, March 4, 2020 – Home Group

In healthy churches, the life of the church isn't limited to Sunday morning. There should be touchpoints of community, service, and learning throughout the week. EIC hosts "home group" meetings on Wednesday nights, where we gather to dive deeper into the text from the sermon, pray, and enjoy each other's company. This week, Patrick and Lyndsay hosted us, along with five others, in their Parisian apartment. It was a beautiful space, classic and elegant. Impressionist paintings hung on the walls above ornamental furniture. Matching old books lined the shelves. A traditional area rug softened the hardwood floors. Their home office could have been in the West Wing.

Patrick, a gentleman with neat brown hair, welcomed us in a dignified southern accent. Originally from Georgia, he attended the Naval Academy before serving as a fighter pilot for twenty years. Now he works as a liaison between the French and American navies. Lyndsay had prepared bruschetta and an array of other fancy finger foods. When a native Parisian joined us, Patrick and Lyndsay parlayed in effortless French.

I looked at Bethany. We were impressed, if not a little intimidated. Proud as we were of our efforts to learn the culture and settle in, these two Americans in Paris were playing an entirely different ballgame.
On the way out, Patrick thanked us for coming, and then paused as if he'd forgotten something.

"Just one second, I have something you might be interested in." He hurried to the kitchen and walked back with a pack of Oscar Meyer bacon! "I'll bet you've missed this stuff living over here. The embassy has a shop where we Americans can stock up on some of the comforts of home you won't find in Carrefour. Bacon, of course, and salsa, root beer, cornbread... all that good stuff. Enjoy, bonne soirée!"

Thursday, March 5, 2020 – Distal Phalanx

The hot plates desperately did not want to work today, so the bacon took nearly an hour to cook, and the eggs another half, but it was worth it. Bethany was back from shadowing in time for us to share an early dinner before practice. I was excited to hear all about her day, even if I understand French better than unfiltered medical speak.

"And then the next one was an arthroplasty, focusing on the glenohumeral joint with an interscalene block, which went well, you should have seen his glenoid cavity, but then there was an emergency thing I got to join him for."

"Uh huh." I nodded, doing my best to follow along.

"It was this sweet old man who got his thumb caught in a machine and they were trying to reattach it. He had these big blue eyes and looked scared and confused, which was sad; I tried to smile at him whenever I could, since he was under local anesthesia."

That was pretty sad. I hate thinking of vulnerable people in pain.

"They were of course concerned about the princeps pollicis artery and reestablishing blood flow, so they drilled two pins in from the top going into the distal phalanx, then applied pressure to the thumb and released the tourniquet to see if it would pink up. And it did! So they reapplied the tourniquet and stitched it back on. They even got most of his nail back on with this awesome cross-stitch."

"Well that's good!"

"Yeah, but then the doctor who explains things to me in English left and the new guy seemed confused about who I was and why I didn't speak French, so I just walked out of the OR and came home."

During practice, I've been calmer lately. Instead of itching to fight when a defensive lineman does something I don't like, I'm starting to shrug it off, make a joke, or even offer a tip if I've got one.

"Hey mix up the hand slap and the bull rush, harder to stop."

"If the tackle leans on you, pull him forward and get outside."

"You're fast enough, quit jumping the snap count, that won't work for long."

This is a better headspace, for all parties involved.

Friday, March 6, 2020 – Rain

It has rained a lot since we arrived. Last night, the rain blew on and off throughout practice. James cursed the rain nonstop, to the point that Brian looked over, concerned. While I doubt I could ever match James' unique disdain for precipitation, I've been more fond of it than expected. I have a theory as to why. Staying with my parents in Grand Rapids over Christmas, we watched *Midnight in Paris.* Owen Wilson's character bubbles about his love for the rain. *It's so romantic! It adds charm! Mystery! Intrigue! I like it better this way!* After that, my expectations were set. Rain was a good thing in Paris! I looked for beauty when the rain started, always assuming I'd find it. Expectations are powerful.

***

James and I sat with Paul in his office, watching practice. Paul hobbled around with more than a simple limp. He stayed out of practice last night, but was eager to play Sunday. He nearly tripped sitting down, wincing in pain.

"Paul, bro, don't feel like you gotta play this week, we got it under control." James looked concerned.

"Yeah, our run game alone should put up fifty points. It's a long season."

"I just hate to miss anything. I will see how I feel. But don't worry, if it is too bad Sunday, I will let

Mattias play." He leaned back and sighed. "Okay, let's watch some of practice."

We were short staffed last night, and at one point, big Sofian stood in at right tackle, trying to catch up with Axwell, our quickest defensive end. I don't think he got a finger on him.

"What you would say to Sofian here? He gives up a sack!"

James and I looked at each other.

"Um, to be honest, I think the biggest coaching point here is to get Washnee to show up and bump Sofian back inside, or dare Axwell to go to the other side."

"Yeah bro he isn't even close."

I don't know how Paul is still surprised when our stalwart defensive line makes it around backup linemen, but I do appreciate the high expectations. He takes responsibility for so much of the program and holds others to the same standards he sets for himself. Unfortunately, few others are willing or able to meet that standard.

Saturday, March 8, 2020 – Seine

In the morning, we took the RER south to a suburb where Bethany got together for brunch with some ladies from church. Uninvited, I strolled the quiet town, looking for a café to read in. Walking down a long hill, I noticed people walking in and out of an alleyway up ahead. Curious, I crossed the street, walked downhill, and turned in with the others. Between two old buildings was the street market I've always wanted to see. Rows of tents with bright vegetables, wheels of cheese, fish neatly lined up on ice, and fresh cuts of meat.

When brunch was done, Bethany met me in a café and we walked towards the southern arm of the

Seine. The earliest hints of spring were in the air and the day was ripe for a stroll. For two hours, we hugged the riverbank, walking into the city. An array of low, flat, houseboats moored along the bank. Closer to the city, under La Périphérique, the boats transitioned from vagabond scraps of metal to the lap of luxury. On a small island, we took a picture with a one-third sized replica of the Statue of Liberty, gifted to the city by the American expats of Paris in the Eighties.

Now in Paris proper, we found a bench in a riverside park and sat down, feeding a pack of pigeons, as one does on a leisurely stroll through the city. They fought ruthlessly for every scrap of bread; the aggression was unbecoming of civilized birds on such a lovely day.

"Tommy, I have a question for you." Bethany looked intently at the fighting birds.

"Anything, up to half of my kingdom."

"Very funny. But this is serious." She looked up at me with an odd look on her face. I wasn't sure if I should be nervous, or was she holding back a smile? "Have you ever seen a *baby* pigeon?"

"Umm, no I.. can't say that I have, now that I think about it. Why?"

"It's because they don't *exist*! And you wanna know *why* they don't exist?"

"Umm.."

"Because pigeons aren't even *real*! They're robots, made by the government to *spy* on us!"

I leaned back, taking in the gravity of this shocking news.

"Oh no, we're *screwed*! Let's get outta here!"

We got back to La Courneuve in time to watch some of the Flash Division II game, sitting in the stands and laughing with Bruno, Brian, and Adil. I kept an eye on Badis, nervous every time he got the ball. Bethany was doing the same. On a third and long, Badis lined up in

252 | GRIDIRON REDEMPTION

shotgun, checked his receivers, and called for the snap. Both his tackles were easily beat, sending him scrambling towards the home sideline, desperately searching for an open man. He spotted a slot receiver in the middle and fired an impressive cross-body throw just as two defenders pummeled him. The ball bounced off the man's chest and into the safety's arms, who took off down the sideline. Badis peeled himself off the turf and made a valiant effort to chase him down, but was nailed back into the ground by a linebacker on a questionable block. His teammates didn't seem quite as concerned with the pick-six.

Afterwards, we waited next to the bleachers for Badis to come out of the locker room. He was disappointed but looked happy to see us.

"Oh guys! Thank you for coming! I am sorry we could not do better."

"We're glad we got to see you!" Bethany knew how to console a defeated football player. "Tough one, but you had some good plays. I'm sure you guys will come together."

"Ugh yes, I hope so too. So many of my teammates are just here for fun, they don't even care that we lose. I feel like I am Oscar, trying to do good work while Andy and Michael make idiot jokes! Sometimes I just want to say, 'Dwight, you ignorant slut!'"

"Hold on a second," I laughed, "you know The Office?"

"Of course! How could I understand American memes if I do not watch this?"

Sunday, February 8, 2020 – Vikings

We arrived at Stade Geo Andre just before 8:30 AM, but the bus didn't leave until an hour later. It was a far cry from the serious road trips I've grown accustomed to. A bit more chaos, and not just at the back of the bus. People were standing in the aisle, shouting across seats, hoots of laughter, Uno games, music blasting, some dancing. Guillaume walked around passing out croissants to the offensive linemen. A bus ride like that can be a great time if you're part of the action, but no one wanted to slow down and translate for us, so after amusedly taking it in for a few minutes, Bethany, James, and I put in headphones.

While a gameday bus in the NFL would never look like this, there are similarities across the board. On the way to the airport before our preseason game in Miami, I sat two rows ahead of Julio Jones and a few others huddled around a Nintendo Switch playing Super Smash Bros. I think I saw Stefan and Mamadi playing the same game today. Jones may earn more in one week than the all-time Flash operating budget, but he wanted to spend his bus ride with the same simple pleasures.

We pulled into Wattignies two hours before the 2:00 PM kickoff. It was a small town with a strip of two story brick buildings and plenty of trees. We filed off the bus, grabbing our bags and heading for a locker room on the other side of the school. The room wasn't big enough for everyone, so the linemen waited outside while the skill players got ready first. Having learned my lesson in the first two games, I picked up snacks at Carrefour yesterday and was happy to pull them out now for a pregame meal of peanuts, a fig bar, and two croissants.

Bethany manned her post at the taping station next to Dr. Momo. Limping around and a bit scattered, Paul scanned the crowd until he saw Bethany and hobbled towards her.

"Whatsup, Bethany? You good?"

"Yeah Paul, how's the toe?"

"Oh, my toe? Its, uhh, not good. But I try to play. Hey I have a question, do you know how to keep the stats for a game?" He held up a binder with a hopeful look on his face. "Bruno will run the camera today, and I don't know who else to ask."

"Uh, yeah, yeah I can do that!" She shot a look in my direction.

"Thank you! This is *huge* help!" He clapped and limped away.

I came over and explained as much as I could before the locker room opened up and I had to get ready.

Jogging out for the warmup with James, I was surprised to see a rugby field, slightly longer and wider than what we're used to. There were some rudimentary lines drawn over the turf, reminding us where to go. By now, our pregame routine was established and crisp. After the dynamic warmup, I led the linemen through a rapid series of blocks to loosen up the pads.

"Search a droit! Okay opposite! A plus, zone a droit! Opposite! Pass pro, solo!"

As soon as the game started, it was clear this was asymmetric warfare. We had them completely outmatched athletically, and it was hard to imagine any scenario where they could have beaten us. We played incredibly sloppy at times, missing assignments and even stringing together four penalties in a row. But even after that, Paul, who managed to play the first quarter before wisely taking himself out, found Doukie for a sixty-yard touchdown.

At halftime, even though we didn't make the long walk back to the locker room, Doukie went off to a more secluded area and bowed for his ritual prayers. I've come to deeply respect him. He has a noble air, and takes pride in leading the team. While our worldviews diverge with entirely different ideas of who God is and how man can mend his relationship with him, I respect his devotion, much more than someone with no convictions at all.

I haven't had such an easy time moving people since high school, but I can't remember the last time I've had this much fun. I knocked a stubby nose tackle down and pushed him back into the turf when he tried to get up. As he looked back up at me in wide-eyed disbelief, I wondered why I was doing the rage thing. I had no reason to play angry today.

That didn't mean I stopped playing hard, of course. On a full slide pass protection, where everyone steps to their left and covers a gap, I had no one to block and heard Coach Cushing's voice echo from deep inside my memory. *FIND WORK!* I looked at the man James had locked away at arm's length and charged, ramming my shoulder into his side, and sent him rolling on his back. James jumped around, absolutely loving it. The ref, however, didn't and told me as much in our huddle. He interrupted Mattias and challenged me.

"Why do you do that?!"

"Excuse me sir?"

"Why you hit him like that?!" He looked up at me scornfully.

"No whistle sir, play was still going."

"The ball was not near you, it was not necessary."

I couldn't believe he wanted to do this right now. I was ready to fire back. *Okay sir, if we're getting Socratic, did you know football is a violent game? That any OL coach in America would give me a gold star for that? That DL didn't have to show up if he didn't want to! Or are you trying to play a softer version of the game over here? And if you didn't like it so much, why not just throw a flag instead of interrupting our huddle?!*

In a moment of reason, I kept my mouth shut. But it bothered me. I felt like a violent mercenary, dropping in on what ought to have been an enjoyable weekend activity. Is this what they wanted when they came out to the rugby pitch today? An oversized twenty-four year old careening around at breakneck speed intent on knocking people down? After having spent a significant portion of his life being trained to do just that?

Either way, the savagery wasn't restricted to James and me. Our entire team was playing on a different level. The defense registered one punishing hit after another.

Bethany occasionally shuffled up behind me, furiously scribbling on the clipboard, trying to keep track of who was in on the tackles.

"There were like five people on him, who do I give the tackle to?!"

I shrugged, not envying her job in the least.

While the refs may have been appalled, the Vikings were fascinated. Between almost every play, we were talking to the defensive linemen, who seemed happy to be there, on the same field with the mighty Flash and their Americans.

"You guys very big! Good hit!"

"You come from America, yes? Welcome to France! You play NFL?"

"You good team, we come to top division, get better soon! We very good division two year before!"

"You stay for beer after game! Very good! Close to Belgium!"

In the fourth quarter, we marched down field on what would be the last drive of the game. On the twenty yard line, Mattias called a screen to the left. In my stance, everything just felt right. The weather was perfect, my mind was clear, my joints didn't hurt.

"Blue dix! Bluuuue-dix-set-hut!"

I snapped into a pass set for one second, punched the defensive end up field, dipped my left shoulder to release inside of him, and ran towards the endzone at top speed. I could feel Guillaume just behind me, finding a lane between my hip and the sideline. A single linebacker stood in our way. I adjusted my angle of attack and met him on the five yard line. He stumbled back but stayed on his feet, intent on closing the lane and forcing Guillaume out of bounds. At the three yard line I dipped and pushed him back with my right arm, keeping the lane open just long enough for Guillaume to slip through and into the endzone. He got up and we yelled in each other's faces while the others joined in the celebration. It was perfect. To the Vikings' credit, they put up a fight and created enough confusion to hold us to a respectable blowout, 41-0. In our one solid quarter, we put up twenty-seven points. If we had our heads on straight for the whole game, we could have scored one-hundred.

Something in the handshake line after the game blew me away. I could hardly wrap my head around it because I had no frame of reference for what I saw. With the helmets popped off, I got my first good look at the men I'd just struggled with. There were, mixed in with twenty and thirty year olds, older men! Not just old as far as young adults go, like Moose, but genuinely old. There were three I would put over fifty years old, one might have been sixty. This may not be old in the grand scheme of things, but on a tackle football field? It was unfathomably ancient.

I imagined the horror of putting all my strength into flattening one of my older uncles. It just seems wrong! Though I can't imagine how, I hope they enjoyed it. I also wonder how sore they'll be after the game. Twenty-two year old seniors give freshmen a hard time if they're sore or injured. *You're too young to be hurt! I wish I had fresh legs like you!* But this? It was a different ball game. How could I ever complain about a sore hip to them?

Inside, we slowly filed through the four showerheads, steam drifting into the unheated locker room. I packed up my gear and put on a black Flash polo. We stood around in the parking lot, waiting for our bus while the sun got low in the sky. It was just warm enough to feel comfortable without a jacket. Bethany and I shared our remaining snacks and politely declined a few cigarettes. We picked the front seat of the bus this time, but it didn't matter; the team was asleep before we got to the highway. I leaned back and watched the dark orange sun set over a green field packed with wind turbines, Bethany sleeping on my shoulder.

We were getting comfortable enough to show others around the city.

The last scoring drive of my life, though I didn't know it at the time.

CHAPTER VII

Dark Clouds

Monday, March 9, 2020 – The Enemy

We took it slow today, sleeping in, reading, working out, and spending some time enjoying the McDonalds high speed internet. Later at the office, it was a typical film session: half the group looking at their phones, a bag of candy making its rounds, and Paul battling the WI-FI. He pushed the group but kept things light.

After a French comment that drew laughs, he turned to James and me with a translation.

"I just tell them, after the game the Vikings coach says to me he is excited for the season because they have a very young team. I try not to laugh, but *excusez-moi?!*" Apparently he'd seen the senior Vikings too.

On the tram ride back, two middle school aged girls struck up a conversation with Bethany, each side doing their best to dabble in the other's language. They asked Bethany if they could look at her wedding ring, ooing and ahing when she obliged. Bethany asked if they played any sports and they proudly showed her the soccer jerseys in their backpacks. Then they asked where we were from.

"Je suis de Les Etats-Unis."

"Ahh." A look of recognition. "Yes, I know. The enemy of Iran!"

What?! I couldn't believe that was her first thought. The animosity was certainly in the news these days.

Sitting in our little room later, I felt rich. I was sitting with my beautiful wife, eating a bar of dark chocolate and watching *The Last Samurai*. But I got to wondering where we stood financially. Some quick math suggested we were doing alright. Between the salary and covered living expenses, we're taking in around two-thousand Euros monthly. Not much, but in a way, more than you might expect. Most weeks, I only work about twelve hours. When we have a game, it could be much more, but I'd do that for free, so we'll leave it out. Nor will I count workouts, for the same reason. This means I'm being paid roughly fifty dollars per hour. If I worked the same number of hours as an entry level consultant or investment banker – seventy is a conservative estimate, I went to school with plenty of them – I would be making $182,000 per year, about on par with their salaries. Factor in the ability to travel to Luxembourg for two-hundred dollars, and I dare say we come out on top in this deal.

Tuesday, March 10, 2020 – Burn Notice

Staying in my grandpa and grandma's condo in Holland, Michigan, the last of week of July in 2010, I would sneak out to the porch after everyone else had gone to sleep and pull up my favorite show on our silver portable DVD player. Burn Notice is about Michael Weston. He used to be a spy, until he got burned and was left to his own devices in Miami. There, he used his unique skillset to take on unsuspecting criminals, helping the common man, making some extra cash, and trying to figure out how he got there.

I distinctly remember the DVD's main menu. Michael and his friends posed, well dressed and confident. A happy and adventurous guitar song played in the background. I'd get an ambiguous feeling of longing for Michael's situation. Was it wonder? Envy? Fascination? I didn't know at the time, but I think I have an idea now. Michael was in Miami, doing something unconventional and exciting. His life was full of freedom and intrigue, but he had to earn his way into this situation. Before Miami, he had to rise through several rigorous structures, mastering the basics of his evolving craft. First he joined the Army, attending schools, gaining experience, and rising the ranks until he was an elite special forces operator. Then, he joined the CIA and spent years rising that ladder. Only then was he even qualified for this unconventional life in Miami. He couldn't have dreamt where he'd end up when he shipped off to boot camp, but every step along the way prepared him for an opportunity he didn't know existed.

Watching this in Holland years ago, I was enjoying an anxious week off before high school football training camp started. It felt like I had such an immense task ahead of me, a mountain I doubted I could climb. What would become of giving so much of myself to football? I didn't know what the destination was, but it felt so far off. Looking at Michael Weston, cool and confident, I think I was jealous that he was on the other side of his mountain. He rose the ranks into the great unknown and I was just getting started.

Fast forward to tonight after practice and I felt a kinship with Michael Weston. I had put in so much work to rise the ladders of American football, but was booted from the top one earlier than expected. That left me here, in a place I never planned on coming, but now had no interest in leaving. Having a great time in obscurity. Off of the highway I had been on for years, but in a place that I could never have reached without my time on the highway. Perhaps how Weston felt in Miami? I don't know if this melodrama will make sense to anyone else, but I laughed to myself, kneeling there listening to Niko talk, having just cracked an age old code.

Wednesday, March 11, 2020 – Boulogne

With an hour before EIC home group started, Bethany and I ambled around Bois de Boulogne, a massive park outside of the Sixteenth. Once a royal hunting ground, the plot offered a refreshing dose of nature that brought peace to an increasingly chaotic world. Just today, the World Health Organization had declared COVID-19 a pandemic. That word changed everything. It seemed better suited for dystopian science fiction movies. Suddenly, no one felt safe. I'm sure it was imagined, but the streets seemed quieter; there was an eerie chill in the air.

Home group was a block away in Ann and Henry's apartment, just down the road from the Arc de Triomphe. Ann and Henry were Parisian natives in their eighties and came of age under Nazi occupation. I shuddered at the thought.

They buzzed us into the apartment building and were waiting at the door while we walked up the steps. Ann wore a floral frock, Henry brown slacks and navy sweater. Ann held out a bottle of hand sanitizer and offered an elbow bump. Social distancing, a new term to most of us, may be one of the premier strategies for mitigating the impacts of the virus, but it will certainly prove to be one of the most distressing. Everyone was timid, afraid to get too close. We were in the midst of a new reality that was rapidly changing how we could connect with one another. *How quickly things change.*

The joy came in turning to a loving God, sovereign over everything in our world. We sang "Great is Thy Faithfulness" in their living room, half the group belting out the hymn in French and the rest in English. *Strength for today and bright hope for tomorrow! Blessings all mine, with ten thousand beside!* In his retirement, Henry passes out Bibles with the Gideons and clearly loves the Lord deeply. It was his idea that we sing to worship the Lord amidst the ever deepening uncertainty.

Thursday, March 12, 2020 – Crashing Down

I must have forgotten to plug my phone in last night, because my alarm never went off and I slept in. I got up and looked at my watch - 10:15. *Ugh, another late start!* Oh well, we were up pretty late after coming back from home group. As I brushed my teeth, Bethany looked intently at her phone in bed.

"Hey come here when you're done. I've got something, or, *things*, I guess, to tell you." She didn't look up. She sounded serious.

I lay back in the bed, careful not to flop and break through the frail frame.

"What's up?"

"Well first of all, I had a dream that Russian kidnappers came to Marengo and took someone who was pretending to be my mom... that's less important. I guess a lot happened last night."

"Like what?"

"The AIA Puerto Rico spring break trip got canceled, the NBA suspended its season indefinitely, the Big Ten Tournament got canceled, Trump banned all travel to Europe for thirty days."

"What?! This all just happened?"

"Also, Tom Hanks and his wife tested positive."

"Not Hanks!"

"And the tiger at the Bronx zoo, for what that's worth."

For the first time, everything seemed up in the air. Can we go to Stockholm next weekend? Barcelona in April? Will we play in London in May? Could my family still come? I realized how much I had been looking forward to their visit. A chance to show off what we've discovered in France and explore the Netherlands, our ancestral homeland, together.

I poured a glass of water and sat down at the desk, opening my computer to check on our stocks. I about choked on it when I saw the red. If only we had some cash to buy the dip. But then again, as we enter the first bear market of our adult lives, who the heck knows how much further it will go?

Practice changed on pace with the rest of the world. We showed up like normal, watching film with Paul and going over the practice plan. Bethany sat in the hallway, filling out an application to get pre-approved for a home loan. Bruno walked into Paul's office, a worried look on his face.

"I just hear from La Courneuve mayor of new restrictions. We have to cancel practice tonight."

We hadn't gone through five more plays when he hurried back in.

"Okay now I talk to general manager of Corsaires and he wants that we cancel the game on Sunday."

Paul halfheartedly tried to keep playing the video, his brown eyes clearly distracted. Predictably, now, Bruno came back.

"The league managers just send out an email, there will be no games or practices until March twenty-five. Also, the president will address the nation tonight."

Everything was changing so fast. Two days ago, everyone said goodbye with the customary handshake and hug. Now, we said goodbye with elbow bumps and foot touches.

A few others stuck around with us in the Flash office until President Macron came on screen from the Elysée Palace. He looked very serious. Doing my best to follow along, and occasionally asking Badis for help, it seemed like a classic crisis response speech. Unifying and resolute. Grave, but confident in the next steps. Understanding of the sacrifice he was asking for. Work from home, wash your hands. The virus has no passport, no one is safe.

The French American Football League wasn't the only one affected. Updated cancelations poured in by the minute. The NBA, NCAA, MLB, all stopped. The XFL didn't make it through the inaugural season. It dawned on me that I may have played my last down of football.

I couldn't keep up with the notifications. Music festivals, church services, restaurants, you name it. All canceled. I haven't seen anything like this in my lifetime. I was in kindergarten during 9/11, but that didn't even compare.

Bruno handed me the keys to the car on the way out.

"I am not sure when we see you again, but here is the car, so you can get to places. If anything go wrong, if the power go out, if there is violence, I write down my address and you can come to our house. We will stay in touch to help you however you need. Good luck."

With that, we left the office and sped back on the quiet streets. Safely inside Chambre 12, I connected my phone to a speaker and cued up, "It's The End of the World As We Know It." Bethany poured glasses of cheap red wine and we danced ardently around the lamplit room.

Friday, March 13, 2020 – What's Going On?

We spent most of the morning scanning articles about the virus. Everything escalated so quickly and the dramatic changes around the world were surreal. What was a tertiary concern a few days ago hasn't just become the main thing, it's the only thing. I read about prospects for the stock market, the science behind coronaviruses, and the race for a vaccine.

For the first time in my lifetime, the entire world had, for all intents and purposes, zeroed in on one problem. Of all the impossible things humans did on a daily basis, what could we accomplish with all our energy and resources pointed in one direction? Perhaps only an alien invasion could do more to unify the world in a moment's notice. I wonder if we'll stay together.

The afternoon introduced us to a strange contradiction. We had absolute freedom over our time, but so little freedom over what to do with it. As of noon today, we weren't supposed to travel at all, unless absolutely necessary. No last minute trip to Normandy.

With Fitness Park closed, Bethany and I walked to one of Stade de Mode's turf fields, making up a circuit of sprints and body weight exercises in the warm sun. *Twenty-five pushups, ten burpees, fifty split squats, then run to the goal and back, ten rounds.* A gentle breeze blew through the air. It reached sixty degrees in the midafternoon when we lay back and stretched. How could the world be in such dire straits when this corner was so peaceful?

We had two weeks of this to look forward to, but really, there was no end in sight. No one knew if or when the downward spiral would stop.

Saturday, March 14, 2020 – Tulip Festival

We spent the day around Stade de Mode, the walls getting just a bit smaller. Niko sent the team a message, encouraging us to do our part and stay home. He hoped we could be together soon. I suppose I'm still a professional football player, but the future loomed, and I worked on an application for the Army Reserve.

Dinner may prove to be the highlight of our isolated days. I cooked chicken with freshly chopped garlic cloves, simmered in olive oil, salt, pepper, and herbs. Bethany made a dill potato-leek soup.

After dinner we talked to my parents about their trip plans. The itinerary was technically safe, considering the thirty-day travel ban, and their flights hadn't been canceled. But could we really count on things getting back to normal by then?

I wrestled with self-pity for a while. What if the things we're looking forward to don't happen? For the first time, I saw the possibility on the table. A warm coffee shop in Stockholm after a fjord boat tour, walking through a castle in Prague, exploring Tulip Festival in Amsterdam, evening tapas in Barcelona, a night train to Budapest, French national champions, European champions, dinners with Badis and film sessions with Paul... It was hard to admit, but I'm not entitled to any of these experiences.

In high school, one of my teammates was shot and killed in Grand Rapids, shortly before leaving to start a college football career. In an unforgettable eulogy, his pastor asked the packed church to consider James 4:13-16.

"Come now, you who say, 'today or tomorrow we will go into such and such a town, spend a year there and trade and make a profit' – yet you do not know what tomorrow will bring. What is your life? For you are a mist that appears for a little time and then vanishes. Instead you ought to say, 'if the

*Lord wills, we will live and do this or that.' As it is, you boast
in your arrogance. All such boasting is evil."*
    What is your life?

Sunday, March 15, 2020 – Pole Position

"Hey guys?" Badis asked while we ate our cereal
and yogurt. "Do you think you can drive me to Gare de
Lyon? My parents asked me to come home to Grenoble,
because my work is closed and we have no practice with
the Flash."

"Yeah of course, we've got nothing going on."

"Thank you." He looked down solemnly. "I hope
I will be back in two weeks, but I buy one way ticket just
in case."

"I'm sure we'll see you again." I tried to smile,
but was kicking myself. I don't like making promises I
might not be able to keep.

The drive took less than twenty minutes this time.
Spaces that once hummed with life looked abandoned.
Gates were closed and windows shuttered. We pulled up
in front of the grand old train station and Badis got out.
Unsure whether a handshake or hug would be appropriate,
we waved goodbye and talked like we'd see him soon.

We stopped by Carrefour on the way back. Arriving
fifteen minutes before it opened at 9:00 AM, a crowd of
people fidgeted by the gate, like race cars vying for the
pole position.

Bethany and I stood off to the side, practicing a
Bible passage we were memorizing together. At nine, the
gates opened and the line sprinted into the store.

"I thought that only happened on Black Friday
and in apocalypse movies." Bethany stared at the chaos.

By the time we went in, the toilet paper shelf was
spotless, and most of the canned food was gone. I was

genuinely relieved to see people line up and wait at the checkout. What if one person decided not to pay and mob mentality brought everyone else along? For the first time in my life, it felt like societal order was hanging on by a thread.

I thought back to a time I'd seen the power of a mob firsthand. When numbers alone overwhelmed the established order of power. After the Bears signed me for the second time, Coach Hiestand told the offensive line to show up at a youth clinic in Lake Forrest being put on by Olin Kruetz, the legendary Bears center. It was a strange camp. A mass of wealthy elementary students who couldn't care less about their coaches' impressive accolades. They would have been just as content running around a field with their dad's supervising.

Towards the end, it was decided there ought to be a tug-of-war. I can't imagine a more formidable tug team than fifteen NFL offensive linemen. The ultimate combination of size, strength, and athleticism; the cream of all crops. 320lbs on average and faster than anyone off the street. How many fifty-pound children would it take on the other side of the rope to defeat this juggernaut? Apparently somewhere around seventy was enough. There was scarcely room for another boy to grab on, and they dug in with everything they had. The rope moved slowly but decisively in their direction. They bested us!

Monday, Mach 16, 2020 – Contagion

Last night we gave in and did it. We watched *Contagion*. I knew it was a bad idea, but couldn't resist. The 2011 thriller was scary enough when I saw it in high school, but last night? The overlap with our world blurred all lines of reality. Since the pandemic started, I've received all my information through a screen. This screen was more of the same: a bat, a pig, a human in the far east. Social distancing, schools closed, a race to develop a vaccine. What part of this was supposed to be fiction?

The grimmest part of the movie was the breakdown in social order. Fear led to chaos, as looters trashed grocery stores and bands of home invaders terrorized once quiet streets. It was every man for himself. Police officers and nurses stayed home; no one was safe. Were we living in the early minutes of the movie? Or in a kinder, gentler version?

I had to beat back my fears with whatever facts I had at my disposal. Despite the similarities, *Contagion* wasn't reality. In the movie, the virus was a death sentence. Early statistics said COVID-19 wasn't as bad, especially in healthy patients. But no one really knew. If nothing else, we were trying to protect the most vulnerable in society.

Last time I watched this movie I could step outside and relax, seeing that all was well. Not so today. Outside I see lines of people in masks, hoping the grocery stores don't run dry. I get news notifications warning of lockdowns nearing martial law. The gnawing fear hasn't left.

As the sun lowered in the sky, Bethany and I took a walk around the neighborhood. Starting at midnight, it would be against the law to leave your home without an official printed pass stating you were on official business or going to the grocery store. We have no precedent for any of this. The world was completely different the last time such a pandemic made its rounds. No one can confidently say what will happen next or how it will end. Everyone's just doing their best.

Tuesday, March 17, 2020 – Schedule

We needed discipline to use the time well and keep our cool. We made the bed, changed our clothes, shaved, and cleaned the floors. We made a schedule for the day and stuck to it, for the most part.

0900– wake up, pray, small breakfast
1000– Bible, scripture memory
1200– run, exercise, stretch
1300– lunch, spaghetti and beef sauce
1400– study, read, French practice
1900– dinner, chicken drumsticks and salad
2030– journal, music, call friends/ family, check news
2200– movie/ entertainment
0100– lights out

Stade de Mode is a blessing. Without technically leaving our home, we have acres of fields and trees to ourselves. The space and peace of the natural world beats a suffocating Twitter feed in our small room.

I read that Dr. Anthony Faucci, America's top infectious disease expert and the de-facto leader of the coronavirus response, used to run seven miles per day when he was tackling HIV/AIDS. Asked if he stuck to that schedule now, he replied that due to 19 hour work days, he had to cut it to 3.5 miles per day. At age 79. What a beast! I decided we should run 3.5 miles per day in solidarity with him.

Hearing about his hours gave me an odd feeling. I wasn't "the man in the arena" at the moment. Other people were giving everything they had to save the world and I was on the sidelines. I understood why, but the nagging feeling reminded me that our purpose isn't to enjoy leisure, but to work. Until I get a chance to join the good fight, I'll stay out of the way.

Wednesday, March 18, 2020 – Zoom?

Few things are more frustrating than staring at a spinning circle on a screen. I resolved to never skimp out on good WI-FI in the future. We planned a Google Hangout with my family, brushing off Julie's idea that we try a trendy upstart called Zoom.

I smiled when faces finally popped up on the screen. It felt like we were together, and as long as that was true, I figured we'd be just fine. My older sister Kelly and her husband Mark followed my dad's footsteps into broadcast journalism, and told us about the renewed purpose they feel in their work, keeping the public informed but calm. With all of the misinformation floating around, there has been an increased appetite for veritable journalism, and their website hits have gone through the roof.

Everyone has been adjusting on the fly. At my dad's station, field reporters never enter the building and the whole building is disinfected between shifts. Jimmy and Julie moved to online classes.

I've been thinking about how stable my world has been in the grand scheme of things. Of every human ever born, I can't think of too many with a more secure and predictable world, broadly speaking, than a middle class American born in the late twentieth century. Maybe this will be a small taste of what the rest of humanity throughout history experienced, where misery and uncertainty seem to be the rule, not the exception. We won't be the first to survive and thrive when things fall apart. Maybe I'll look back on these thoughts someday and scoff. *So dramatic!* But I'm just being honest in the here and now.

Thursday, March 19, 2020 – Watches of the Night

In the dead of night, Bethany woke up restless and not feeling well. She held her head and whimpered, feeling warm and nauseous. My heart raced. We felt so alone. Fortunately, it didn't take long before she fell back asleep, blaming the extra salty chorizo egg hash I made for dinner.

Even then, I was awake for a while. We always sleep through the night, so lying awake at three in the morning was strange. What if something really had been wrong? I felt a pang of fear, thinking about the world outside of our dark room. Haunting thoughts of mysterious figures in hazmat suits outside our window, worst case scenarios of being alone in a crumbling world.

I said a prayer and Psalm 64 came to mind.

My soul will be satisfied, when I remember you upon my bed, and meditate on you in the watches of the night; for you have been my help, and in the shadow of your wings I will sing for joy. My soul clings to you; your right hand upholds me.

Turning to Jesus, considering who he is and what he has done, it pushed the fear back. David wrote these words in the wilderness of Judah, and God in his mercy preserved them to comfort and encourage his people for the rest of history. *God is not dead nor does he sleep.*

***

I spent most of the day looking forward to an activity we planned for the night. Around 9:00 PM, James walked into the dining room carrying his thirty-two inch flat screen and set it on top of the microwave. Sotiris heated up a pizza in the toaster oven, Bethany set out chips, and I pulled up *Shawshank Redemption* on my laptop. A good old-fashioned movie night. After a few days with little human interaction, this felt like a wild party. Lael, a tall discus thrower, walked in to grab a meal from the refrigerator, amused by the scene but politely declining to stay. I've hardly seen him since we arrived, but last night he helped me with some French and said he played the violin.

We turned on French subtitles for Sotiris and settled in for the feature presentation. Hope, a hot commodity these days, lies as the heart of the movie and I held back tears when Red walked down the picturesque beach at the end. Sotiris scrolled through Instagram and James was snoring. It was just good to be together.

I lay down feeling much better about the world than after the last movie we watched. It was getting late. Just before I switched off the lamp, there was a frantic knock on our window. Through the translucent glass I saw a blurry figure standing outside. *What?!* I tried to think rationally, but Stade de Mode was supposed to be a secure area, never mind the fact that it wasn't legal to leave your house. My heart raced a bit and Bethany woke up startled. *What person of goodwill would ever knock on our window like that at two in the morning?* Any good feelings from Shawshank Redemption were replaced with the horrors of *Contagion*.

"What's going on? Who is that?" Bethany was as confused as I was.

"I have no clue. I'm going to go outside and check. Umm, stay here I guess and don't open the window? Leave the door open to the hall in case he tries to break in. I'll be right back."

I jogged down the hallway towards the entrance, adrenaline telling me it was time to fight someone. I thought about knocking on James' door, and probably should have, but kept going. Just before stepping outside, I noticed the fire watchman's [1] office was empty. The

---

1 Apparently all dorms and apartments are required to have someone monitor the fire alarms during the night. We had a steady

light was on and his coat was on the chair next to his...
keys. *Wait a minute.* I relaxed and stepped outside.

"Monsieur? Je suis ici!"

The stout old man tromped back to the front door, out of breath and muttering in French, presumably thanking me profusely. I held the door open for him and looked down the building to the right. Our window was the only one with a light on.

Friday, March 20, 2020 – Delegation

Though I can't imagine how we're going to find a house from here, we got pre-approved for a loan! Things in the United States were starting to shut down too, but maybe we could send a family delegation down to Tennessee on a scouting mission. At this point, there was no end in sight to our Parisian adventure.

Saturday, March 21, 2020 – Over

"What does it look like when you are passive aggressive?" Bethany read from the book.

"Ugh, I hate this question. I'd like to think I skip being passive aggressive and just get *aggressive* aggressive when the situation calls for it."

"Virtuous as you think you are, I can assure you that you get passive aggressive too."

While we were dating, I bought *1001 Questions*, a self-explanatory book that was a fun way to get to know one another. Originally I wanted to finish the whole thing before we got engaged, but here we sat, three quarters of the way through. Since it was Saturday, we built some

---

rotation of people who sat in the office watching Netflix, surely keeping one eye peeled for danger.

more free time into the schedule. This afternoon, rumor had it there'd be a spa day.

"Yeah whatever, next question!"

"Do you think aliens exist? Why or why not?"

My phone buzzed, it was a text from Bruno. Bethany noticed I wasn't thinking about extraterrestrial life.

"What's going on?"

"It's Bruno. He said the French league just canceled the remainder of the 2020 season at all levels. He said we should try to get home as soon as possible before all borders are totally closed."

I looked into the same brown eyes I did seven months before outside the aquarium. A look of total connection and understanding. A love strong enough to overwhelm the crushing disappointment in the pit of my stomach.

We embraced, again not sure if we should laugh or cry. Until now, we could hold out hope that things might get better. We could finish the season and pick up where we left off, building friendships and traveling the continent. But we had no unique claim on disappointment. Seven billion other lives were being upended. We were together, healthy, safe, and had a home to run back to. If we could get there.

We spent most of the afternoon on hold with United Airlines, bouncing between overwhelmed customer service lines. Finally, a low and slow American man picked up.

"Heeeeello there Mr.... Doles. What can I do for you?" He sounded like a late night FM radio DJ.

"Hi my wife and I have flights from Paris to Chicago in July, but we need to change them, leaving as soon as possible. Can you help with that?"

"Ooooo. Hm. Paris? To Chicago? That's gonna be a tough one my friend."

"Um, we could also fly to Detroit if that's easier. We just need to get stateside."

"Detroit, huh? That's where I am now. Nice place. Too cold."

"So do you think we could fly there?"

"Oooooh no, you can't fly anywhere in the U.S. right now. Haven't you read the news? You might be in France for a *while* my friend."

"Uh, yeah, yeah I have. Is there *any* way we can get back to the U.S. right now?"

"Weeeeeeeeeell there might be. I'll see what I can do if you hold for a minute."

"That would be great tha-"

'At United, we care about our customers. Fly the friendly skies! An attendant will be with you shortly.'

After twenty minutes of elevator music, my new friend came back on the line.

"Hey hey hey, I got good news for ya. If the Canadians will let you in, you could fly to Chi-town from there."

"Okay that's great. So we fly to Canada, then to Chicago?"

"Well hold on a minute, my friend. I don't know if the Canadians will let you in."

"Oh, um... can you find that out?"

"Ha! I can find pretty much anything out. Just sit tight for a few minutes."

'At United, we care about our customers..'

I sighed and looked over at Bethany. She gave a nervous smile and crossed her fingers.

"Heyyyyy, I'm back. So I called the Canadians. They said you could go through. Well, they said you could today, but didn't make any promises. Either way, I put you on a flight Tuesday. Paris, Montreal, Chicago."

"That's great! Nice work. My wife too, right?"

"Your wife? Brother you didn't mention that part."

"Umm, I definitely di- You know what, sure. Can you get her on the same one?"

"I can take a look. Noooo promises."

'At United...'

I leaned back and rubbed my eyes.

"Bethany we're so close!"

"Yeah, *maybe!*"

Eventually, he was back.

"I did it again. Two flights, Paris, Montreal, Chicago. Tuesday morning. Hope it works."

"Yeah me too, thanks for the help."

United could delay our spa day, but they couldn't cancel it. We turned on some new-age instrumental music, broke out the Dead Sea mud-masks and essential oils, and tried our hands as masseuses. Soon enough, we'd be home. *Maybe!*

Sunday, March 22, 2020 – James

Early in the afternoon, James texted me, inviting me to try one of the New York bagels his parents had smuggled across the Atlantic. Somehow they managed to pack a dozen frozen bagels and a tub of cream cheese.

I joined him in the dining room for a truly remarkable everything bagel.

"Man I always used to think New Yorkers were full of it when they said they had the best bagels, like, how different can they be? But this is really good."

"Yeaaaah bro. I'm *tellin* you! New York does a few things right and bagels are *deeeeefinitely* one of them. They're mad good."

"Yeah, I guess I'm gonna need to find a time to come try the Guilt Trip too!"

"Yes! Dude you gooootta hit Bubba's. That Guilt Trip will get you right."

The unspoken reality was that we were about to leave each other's lives, with little chance of reentering again any time soon. We'd stay in touch, sure, but he'd been a constant companion for the past three months and now that relationship was being pried away. We were both looking down at our bagels.

"Hey," He broke the silence, "did you guys ever do a scavenger hunt at Northwestern?"

"Yeah we did, actually. It was fun, we had to find and do things around the city. We even staged a pretend karate fight in front of this fancy hotel. You should have seen the look on their faces when these guys started throwing karate kicks and stuff!"

"Ha, yeah that's funny." He smiled amiably, like a kindergartener showed him an art project. "We did them too but ours were low-key weirder."

"What kind of stuff did you do?" I asked, unsure if I wanted to know.

"Well, one time we had to kidnap someone on a different team and hold them for five hours in a basement. And then after that you had to puke in the bathroom at this late night bagel shop, then you had ta streak across main street. Then some stuff I shouldn't talk about."

"Woah! That's, um, that's something!"

We sat and talked for a while, wondering what would happen to our teammates. Brian and Adil could probably work from home. Not sure what Sofian and Mamadi would be doing. How was Moose's family? What ever happened to Nyor? Was Washnee messing with us when he said the bus company has him driving hearses now?

When we stood up to leave, James paused and looked down, a shift in demeanor.

"Hey can I ask you something?"

My heart fluttered, hoping he wanted to talk about the Gospel. We had a few conversations, but never that serious.

"Yeah man, anything."

"Do you and Bethany wanna smoke at all? I've got some extra stuff I gotta get rid of before we leave."

Ugh.

"Um, thanks for asking but no."

Monday, March 23, 2020 – Lael

We spent most of the day packing. Seeing the bags piled up in front of an empty wall hurt. I pictured those same bags standing in the Hart's dining room, ready for their trip to France. Who knew they'd be repacked so soon? There's so much purpose in preparing for a voyage, but repacking? It feels destructive. Taking apart what we'd built.

We left our spices and canned goods in the kitchen space, free for the taking. I made an epic portion of potato wedges for dinner and breakfast tomorrow morning. It would feel worse to throw away the totally unused potatoes than to toss a few extra cooked and seasoned wedges. We left the rest of our Samurai sauce in the communal fridge.

Lael walked into the kitchen while I cut the potatoes. At 6'6" 265, I certainly hope he joins the Flash if he doesn't make the Martinique Olympic team. I told him we were leaving tomorrow and he seemed genuinely disappointed. Of all the things that ended just as they started, my friendship with Lael might have been the most fresh. Only in the past couple of weeks had I started talking to him, as his work schedule slowed down with the lockdown.

"You leave... tomorrow!" He repeated in shock.

A renaissance man, Lael spends his free time writing code and uploading instructional violin videos to YouTube. So far, he wasn't confident enough to tell me the name of his channel.

"You come to my room later, and I play you some songs. Please you will come?"

Around nine, Bethany and I knocked on his door. He opened it, grinning ear to ear.

"I'm so glad you come! Please, come, sit." He beckoned, leading us to a small futon in the corner. He pulled a case out from under the bed and opened it, revealing a small electric violin. *No wonder we never heard him practicing!* This time, he plugged it into an amp and started playing elegant scales.

Lael's room was neat and disciplined, but full of character. His native Martinique flag on the wall, a pull-up bar lodged between the doorway, two computer screens on his desk.

"I have idea!" He grabbed a book from his shelf. "I have book of hymns. You find one you know and I can play, you will sing?"

We flipped through and found songs I recognized. *Come Thou Fount, What a Friend We Have In Jesus, Praise God from Whom All Blessings Flow, In Christ Alone, Because He Lives.*

Bethany and I did our best to remember the English words while Lael sang in French, playing the violin from memory and occasionally asking me which note the song started on.

Because He lives, I can face tomorrow. Because He lives, all fear is gone. Because – yeah that's an A, you're right – because I know He holds the future, and life is worth the living, just, because He lives.

It was refreshing and encouraging to worship with him. Afterwards he sent me a text. *That was good. You awake my faith.* He even shared the elusive YouTube channel, so give it a like and subscribe: *7-1 Maestro*.

Tuesday, March 24, 2020 – Leaving

"Hey Paul!"

"Tommy! I hear you are leaving this morning, so I just want to call to say goodbye, since I cannot come to see you and Bethany before you leave."

We lamented the premature end to a good thing. He thanked me for everything I had given to the team.

"When we first talk on the phone, I hang up and say to Bruno. We have to get this guy, I don't care what it takes! You have been the perfect import player. Good guy, good coach, good player."

"Thanks Paul," I was fighting back tears, "Thanks for taking a chance on a married import, I know you had to stick your neck out there to make it work."

"Stick my neck?"

"Oh, um, do extra work, or, make an effort to help. Bethany had such a good time here too and I know you did so much to include her."

"Hey, you two were great combo. Maybe she does more for the Flash than you! By the way, I have some exciting news for you."

"Oh, really? What's up?"

"My girlfriend and I are expecting a baby boy in September! I will not be quarterback next season, just a coach."

"Congrats, Paul! That's so exciting! Will he be the next great quarterback for the Flash?"

"Thank you! And no, I don't think so. He will probably play a sport with more opportunity. Maybe tennis, or soccer."

It was funny, hearing the best French quarterback in a generation recognize the limits of the game he'd given so much of himself to.

We finished packing and sat down for one last meal in Stade de Mode. While we were getting ready to go, Pascal walked in. Over the last week, athletes had slowly been moving out of the dorm, and I wanted to let him know we were next. I asked Google to translate for us, explaining our situation and thanking him for everything he'd done. He looked skeptical when he heard the French translation and spoke into his phone. I got a little nervous. Finally Google spoke back.

"I don't think that you can leave France."

Does he know something we don't? Thankfully Bruno and Mariannick arrived just then and said something that seemed to satisfy him. It was time to go.

We waved goodbye to Mariannick, who would stay back to collect the bedding and kitchen supplies the Flash provided. She wore latex gloves and a white facemask. Masks had become a topic of debate. Did they protect you? Protect others? Should we save them for medical workers who were running out of protective equipment?

With the bags loaded into the trunk, Bruno checked to make sure he had the right paperwork and we got on an empty highway, bound for CDG. James found a flight to New York via Zurich. We pulled over at the United terminal and Bruno helped us with our bags.

"I am sorry it must end like this, and I hope you can make it home with no issue."

"Yeah me too, and thanks for everything, we had a great time. I'll be a Flash fan for life."

"Well you know I say this before, but if you want to come back to play or coach, we will be happy to have you. Just let me know."

"I appreciate that. Au-revoir Bruno."

"James, Godspeed my friend. Hope you make it backalright - we'll stay in touch. see you at Bubba's someday."

"Aight bro, be good be safe."

The airport was a ghost town. Restaurants and duty free gift shops were shuttered and silent. Even without the crowds, check-in took a while. We had our temperatures taken and promised we felt fine and hadn't been knowingly exposed to the virus. At the security checkpoint, a masked agent asked us to keep our distance. Another sprayed down the bin after we pulled our pocket items out. We looked at a board full of canceled flights, almost surprised to see ours was still on. I'd believe we were leaving when we were over the Atlantic.

The wide-bodied 787 might have been a quarter full. Passengers sprawled out across entire rows. A few minutes later, we were in the sky. The flight attendants kept to themselves for the next eight hours, making two quick trips to pass out pre-packaged cold meals. I watched *Rocketman*, a wild fantasy-biopic of Elton John. A product of the mid-nineties, I had no idea his early days were so outrageous.

I got a warm feeling of familiarity when the snow-covered North American landmass appeared beneath us. We landed in Montreal on time. An announcement told us to inform waiting medical personnel if we developed symptoms during the flight. The hazmat team stood ready on our left when we walked off the jet bridge. We passed through security and Canadian customs, moving on to US Immigration. [2]

We sat in a lobby with chairs spread six feet apart, waiting our turn for an interview. Ten minutes later an athletic middle aged man, who may have been ex-military, walked in and called our names. He led us to his office, offering a seat outside of the open door and continuing on to his desk.

"Okay Mr. and Mrs. Doles," he began, looking down at a stack of papers, "how long were you in France?"

---

2   If you're wondering how we pulled that off in Canada, Montreal is one of several airports around the world with forward deployed TSA agents. This means we left Montreal pre-cleared and would land in Chicago as if on a domestic flight.

"Since January seven."

"Okay and what were you doing there?"

"I was playing for a semi-professional football team outside of Paris."

"Football, huh?" He looked up at my frame. "Like, *football* football?"

"Yes sir."

"Hmm. Nice. What was that like? I played in high school."

"Not quite the same, but the guys that play were all in. It was a great time."

"How 'bout that. Well, are you feeling feverish, fatigued, coughing, or unwell in any other noticeable way?"

"No sir, we feel great."

"Alright then, welcome home." He punched down a red stamp.

Boarding another nearly empty flight for Chicago, we talked with the Canadian Airlines flight attendant. They're all on call these days, but getting called less and less. Word was layoffs were on the horizon.

It is hard to picture another airport feeling more like coming home than ORD. While Grand Rapids will always be my hometown, I've only flown out of Gerald R. Ford once, while O'Hare has been the final stop on every other flight I've ever taken.

Coming home was ambivalent; with the world in turmoil, being back felt right. But taxiing to a gate at O'Hare in March? I never imagined that scenario, and it meant something had gone seriously wrong. Bethany and I walked through another barren airport, easily spotting our bags on a sparsely populated conveyor belt.

Outside, it was a relief to see my family. They pulled up in the black Honda Pilot and got out to greet us. My dad would be off of work for two weeks, so none of them seemed to care about social distancing. We hugged and started to catch up while we loaded our bags into the back. My mom packed sandwiches and all of the snacks and drinks we could ask for. There was so much to catch up on, it was hard to know where to start. We jumped back and forth between topics for a while as we drove down 294, until the topic switched to whether or not to stop at Gene and Judes. The answer, of course, was yes. So my first meal back in the U.S. was a double dog with mustard and sport peppers, the best in the world. One person per car was allowed inside, and an employee with gloves opened the door to minimize contact.

On the way back to the highway, we got stuck behind an unmoving train. For ten minutes, we waited. These days, everyone is a little on edge, and we looked around nervously, wondering if the purge was about to begin. It didn't.

Hot dogs finished, we merged back onto the highway and settled in for the ride back to Grand Rapids. Bethany dozed off and I chatted softly with my parents. To the left, the towering Chicago skyline loomed in the night. *Stormy, husky, brawling, city of big shoulders.* I kept an eye on it for a while and then turned ahead. Heading into a scary, uncertain, yet surprisingly hopeful future.

C'est la vie.

French President Emmanuel Macron addressing the nation the night our season was suspended.

The scariest thing was not knowing what fear would do to society.

Epilogue

Fall, 2020

There's something attractive about the idea of settling down in peace after an adventure. At the end of a dramatic southern odyssey in *O Brother Where Art Thou*, George Clooney's character wistfully informs his wife, "I'm awful pleased that my adventuring days have come to an end. Time for this old boy to enjoy some repose." In my melodramatic moments I resonate with him, thinking of the slower pace I ought to enjoy now, after the whirlwind of a football career.

And then I'll laugh. Because I'm twenty-four years old, lacking both the means to retire and any interest in doing so. But I'm certainly not against catching my breath. That's what I'm doing right now, sitting on the back deck of a duplex we bought in East Tennessee, overlooking a green slope down to the hollow that rises up into rolling hills, covered in trees that just barely show their orange intention of shedding leaves in the coming weeks. The sun sets behind the trees next to our house, shading the balcony but illuminating the hills with a fiery golden hour. There's a swelling chorus of frogs and crickets and a gentle breeze attending to the evening.

I thought I could have written the rest of this story from a cafe in the Latin Quarter back in February, but this isn't a bad spot to do it. The world remains ill, but there are signs of healing. The dark cloud isn't so dense, even if we aren't sure when the sun will break through. In this new corner of the world, we have as much peace as we can expect. Bethany hit the ground running with medical school and spends her days peering into cadavers, memorizing endless metabolism pathways and gene mutations, and practicing her newfound osteopathic treatment skills on a very willing subject.

I've been running around the hills and hollers with the local volunteer fire department, trying to read the books I didn't get to in Paris, and getting ready to ship out to Army Basic Training in a few months; Lord willing, they'll turn me into a confident and shrewd Civil Affairs Specialist by next summer. I'm down to 210 pounds, and none of my clothes fit. We also have a new friend living with us, an American Black Lab puppy – Margot[1]. An old fire department vet asked if she was gonna be a "pot licker or a biscuit eater," to the roaring laughter of the rest of the crew. I still don't know what that means, but we sure do love her, accidents and all.

Perhaps now is a good time to circle back to Robert Frost and the questions he raises, not just for high school students but for all of us - do our choices matter? Where do the other roads lead? I'm thankful to accept a source of truth I believe to be far more solid than Frost's musings, brilliant as they are. While I believe the Bible is the source of all things good and true, I've learned to let go of the idea that it will tell me A or B on any given decision, because I'm never promised that in its pages. "Man

1 A French name from the word "Pearl"

plans, God laughs," I can hear my Grandpa saying. Jim Niewiek showed everyone who knew him a better way, as ALS slowly stole his strength away. Follow what you know is right, make the best choice you can when it's uncertain, and keep smiling when it's not what you hoped for, because you know there's a loving God in control whom you'll meet someday. So as the constellations start to twinkle through the fading sunset, I think I'll just sit back and enjoy the beauty of it all while I wait for the next round of adventure.

Settling down in the hills of Tennessee.

Acknowledgements

"Every man should plant a tree, have a child, and write a book. These all live on after us, ensuring a measure of immortality." Or so said Jose Martí, a nineteenth century Cuban poet. I guess I can check one of these off the list. Actually, after finding this quote, I bought a twenty-dollar apple tree from the grocery store and planted it in our backyard. Two thirds of the way there. I'm sure the child will prove to be a more monumental undertaking down the road. This is of course a wildly simplified take on the meaning of life and an overestimation of the importance of this book (and the apple tree), yet at the end of an unexpectedly grueling process, it almost feels justified.

I used to skim through the acknowledgements, if not skip the section altogether. However, after taking on this project, I'll always take the time to appreciate this often overlooked gesture of gratitude. Even a relatively simple book like this wouldn't have happened without a team. Let me emphasize that once more – the book you're holding simply wouldn't exist without the people thanked here, and a host of others I didn't include.

But before this book could happen, there had to be a football career. Thank you to all of the teammates I have ever played with. It is hard to describe how much your teammates mean to you, or how much you'll miss their fellowship when you hang up the cleats. Football is a fun game, but retiring isn't agonizing because I'll miss running around in tight pants and bashing my head in, but because of the joy of comradery. I hope this book serves as a testament to the true bliss of the game. The "hard to put your finger on" beauty that's still there when the money and crowds are gone.

Thank you to my coaches, whose influence has shaped me more than anyone's but my parents. Thank you to Coach Hines, Tolonen, Kuiper, VanderWeide, DeVos, Korhorn, and Faulkner who kindled my passion in youth football. Thank you to Coach Brandt, Semple, Jeremy Fellows, Ross, Dixon, Tittiriga, and especially Don Fellows, who made high school football the time of my life and gave me an opportunity to pursue the game further. Thank you to Coach Cushing, who cared enough to push me to be my best at Northwestern, Coach Hankwitz, who recruited me to become a Wildcat, Coach McCall, Coach Hooten, the athletic training staff, and finally Coach Fitzgerald, the finest leader I've had the privilege of being around. Thank you to Bob Engler, the best agent I could ask for, who gave me an opportunity to pursue a dream, and will remain a friend forever. Thank you to coaches Hiestand, Raiola, Nagy, Morgan, Kronenberg, and Quinn, who gave me an opportunity to play in the NFL, and invested in me while I was there. Finally, *merci beucoup* to Paul, Bruno, and the Flash staff for bringing me across the pond for the best adventure I could ask for to finish my career. You helped redeem this silly game just in time before it ended.

Back to the book, thank you to Stephen Shull, whose encouragement after reading a few journal entries convinced me a book could be worth writing. To John Liverance, for lending his hypercreative mind as a sounding board for ideas, and providing invaluable feedback on the first draft. I talked to him about the book more than anyone else throughout the process. To my sister Julie, who lent her skills in graphic design, formatting, and marketing. Without her, you'd be reading a Word document, or perhaps a spiral bound notebook. To my mom, Susan Doles, for responding to the journal entries I emailed her as updates during our time abroad and for pouring over every word of the first draft (few would argue she's the best writer in our family), though as any acknowledgement worth its two pages will note, any remaining errors are entirely my own. To my dad, Jack Doles, for his feedback on the draft, kind words in the foreword, and showing me from a young age that sports can be so much more than talking heads yelling about stat lines and contracts.

To Bethany, my best friend and love forever, who happily lived out of a suitcase during our first year of marriage. And finally, to Jesus, the giver of all good gifts, my creator, savior, and ultimate hope for eternity, who alone gives me more to live for than a book, tree, or child ever could.

Made in the USA
Coppell, TX
02 May 2022

77343024R00173